OCEANS

EXPLORING THE HIDDEN DEPTHS
OF THE UNDERWATER WORLD

CONTENTS

FOREWORD

A POLAR BEAR LUMBERED PAST ME as I stood on the bow of the *Lance*, a north Arctic research vessel and my home for the past three weeks, to survey the heavens. It was 3 a.m. but in the land of the midnight sun I was staring into a near-perfect summer sky, while being surrounded by a stark, white desert of ice.

Securely ensconced in pack ice just a few hundred miles south of the North Pole, I reflected that a year-long odyssey around the oceans of the globe was coming to an end. From Mexico to Eritrea, from the Arctic down to Tasmania we had explored and documented some of the oceans' deep, dark mysteries – no small undertaking for our team: Paul Rose, a fearless diver, explorer and expedition leader; Tooni Mahto, an intrepid oceanographer and marine biologist; Lucy Blue, a pioneering maritime archaeologist and me. Together we had embarked on a great adventure underpinned with serious scientific ambition.

Bathed in a polar glow, my mind wandered back a few months when, off the coast of Sudan, I was staring down rather than up, into the shimmering moonlit waters of the Red Sea.

Coming face to face with five enormous sperm whales or being surrounded by hundreds of giant, cannibalistic Humboldt squid, these expeditions with the *Oceans* team had seen their fair share of excitement. But Sudan had special significance for me. Not 45 years earlier my father Philippe Snr, an accomplished diver who died in a seaplane crash before I was born, explored these waters. Sitting under the same stars that once looked down on my father, I found myself wondering what he was thinking during his great undersea adventure. Did he share the same hopes and dreams for the future of our planet as I? Did he know a similar fear for what might occur if we did not fight harder for a sustainable future? He once wrote, 'Adventure is where you lead a full life.' Well, this year has been a full life indeed.

Of course, these expeditions have raised similar questions for all of us. We had faced some of the greatest challenges of our lives and somehow not only survived but became stronger. We were a team united by the bonds of shared passion for exploration. Tooni called it a pilgrimage and that seemed to fit. For us the oceans not only stirred a sense of adventure but washed over our very souls.

The oceans are the life support system of this planet. They regulate climate, provide the primary food source for over two billion people and contribute up to

70 per cent of the oxygen we breathe. They cover two thirds of our world and yet we have explored less than five per cent of them. As the author Arthur C. Clarke once remarked, 'How inappropriate to call this Planet Earth when clearly it is Planet Ocean.'

But our exploration came with a psychological price as we witnessed first hand the heavy toll that humanity has wrought on this planet. From tuna farms in the Mediterranean and the shark fin harvest off Mozambique to the thinning ice cap of the Arctic, the oceans are changing rapidly and humankind bears the burden of blame.

While this year has been an amazing adventure for me the best aspect of it all was a chance to share it with the rest of the world. Through film we have captured rare glimpses of some of the greatest phenomena and wonders that lie beneath the waves. In hindsight I think that the more we learned, the more we felt a sense of urgency to tell these stories before it is too late. The consequences of ignorance, like those of irresponsibility, can be fatal. It is my sincere hope that through this work we will make more urgent still the chorus of voices crying out to save the oceans among a new generation connected by a common dream, a universal hope and united by our search for a better tomorrow.

Philippe Cousteau

Summer 2008

INTRODUCTION

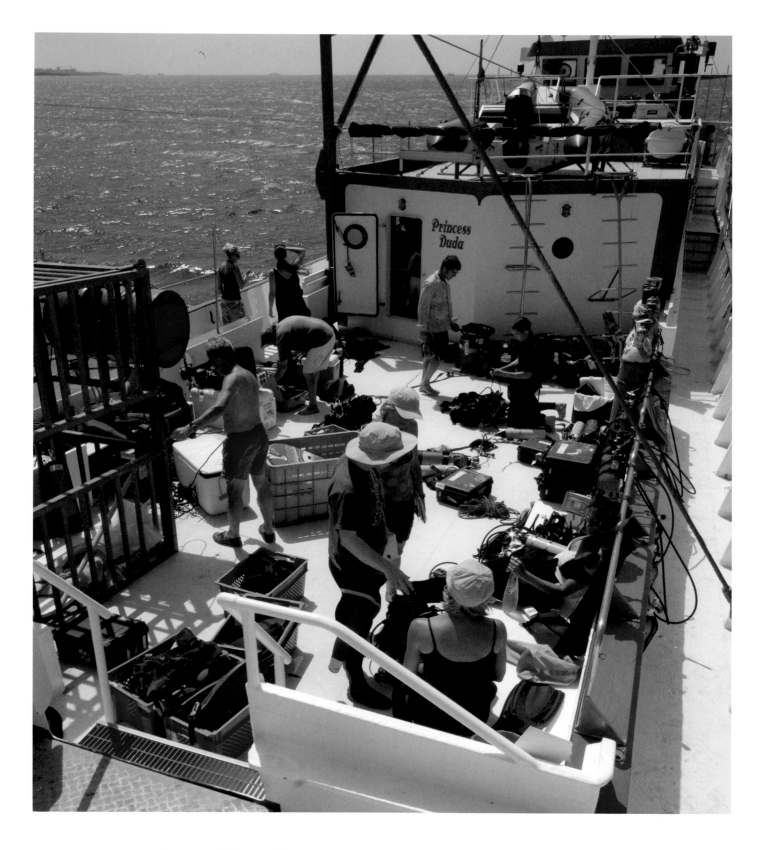

IT WAS THE FIRST DAY of a meticulously planned, year-long quest to reveal the secrets of the planet's oceans and immediately we'd hit a problem. A 25-strong team with 150 heavy boxes of technical gear, 40 suitcases and a shark cage was gathered on the harbourside ready to board, but the dive boat that was to be our home and transport for the next 15 days was nowhere to be seen. A boat is pretty fundamental to the success of any venture focused on the planet's oceans but *Princess Duda* was still several days away, chugging ponderously through the Mediterranean. It was an inauspicious start to a bold endeavour that would lead to cutting-edge exploration of the seas and oceans of the world. There was just the tiniest, barely acknowledged slither of concern that perhaps this entire venture was a tad too ambitious.

… a remarkable adventure … that was mesmerizing, sometimes hazardous and largely unknown.

A year later and we all agreed that the mission had indeed been audaciously ambitious. We had laboured through storms, illness, equipment failures, life-threatening accidents, and close encounters with hostile military. But despite all that, no one on the trip would have swapped a single moment. It was a remarkable adventure that took us into the realms of an underwater world that was mesmerizing, sometimes hazardous and largely unknown. We were pushing back the boundaries of our personal knowledge in unseen oceans as well as extending scientific knowledge.

HOW LITTLE WE KNOW

To most of us, seas and oceans are flat, featureless expanses. On a good day, the vast mirrored surfaces stretching endlessly towards the horizon provide a picturesque foil for a sunset. Yet these glassy surfaces hide an utterly extraordinary world inhabited by curious creatures that are often rare and elusive. The seas teem with life, which barely causes a surface ripple. Four fifths of all life on earth is found below the waves and there is still much to be discovered in the depths of the deep blue. There are mountains that dwarf the Himalayas, waterfalls bigger than Niagara and more active volcanoes than anywhere else on the planet. Beneath the South Pacific in 1993 scientists located the largest known concentration of active volcanoes, a group of 1133 volcanic cones and seamounts in an area the size of New York State. The mid-ocean ridge, a chain of mountains that runs through all the great oceans, is 37,300 miles long, with an average height of 3000 metres above the ocean floor. Together, the oceans make up an unimaginably vast environment wrapping around more than 70 per cent of the surface of the planet.

OPPOSITE *Several days later than planned, the Oceans team loaded its technical gear, luggage and a shark cage on to the* Princess Duda. *When the ship finally got underway, it marked the start of a year-long quest to investigate and report on the health of seven of the world's seas and oceans.*

PREVIOUS PAGE *Four fifths of all life on earth is found under the seas, which cover more than 70 per cent of the planet. The team set out to investigate this extraordinary nether world in eight expeditions which included more than 1000 dives.*

This is the world we scan with barely a second thought during flights or voyages to foreign destinations. It's on the edge of our consciousness. But the seas have always been vital for mankind. They have shaped our history and now our very survival depends on them. The seas and oceans allowed global exploration, which assisted immeasurably in the progress of the major civilizations. Their rich harvest steered commercial growth from ancient times and the seas helped to model political destinies, being the theatres for decisive battles.

Today, the oceans provide over half the oxygen we breathe, via the photosynthesis of millions of tonnes of microscopic plankton. The marine life the seas sustain provides food and livelihood for billions of people. Ocean currents drive the weather and climate system of every country in the world.

As for the future, rising sea levels are threatening many coastal populations. Salt waters are becoming more acidic due to the absorption of greater amounts of carbon dioxide and this is damaging the marine food chain. Meanwhile, warming seas could trigger a change in the ocean systems that maintain our climate, perhaps causing a devastating catastrophe that inevitably accompanies extreme weather.

And yet, despite its pivotal importance, remarkably little is known about the wilderness of our oceans. Indeed, we know more about the surface of Mars than the deep ocean floors. Scientists estimate that there may be as many as a million new species out there waiting to be discovered and, while the dry lands of the earth are now almost completely known, the vast majority of the sea bottom is unmapped and unexplored.

THE *OCEANS* EXPEDITION

Given this lack of knowledge, it seemed like a perfect time to launch a series of global ocean expeditions to probe at least some small part of the planet's seas. It proved to be an irresistible project and we were able to assemble a crack team of ocean experts. Explorer and expedition leader Paul Rose, ex-base commander of the British Antarctic Survey and dive trainer to the US navy; renowned maritime archaeologist Lucy Blue; marine biologist and oceanographer Tooni Mahto; and conservationist Philippe Cousteau, grandson of the well-known underwater pioneer Jacques Cousteau. All have individual specialist expertise but they are united by one thing: a lifelong passion for the sea. As Tooni Mahto put it, 'When I was a kid, I wanted gills. Other kids wanted wings – I wanted gills.'

It was a bold, almost excessively bold undertaking. Over the course of a year we set up eight separate expeditions to seven different seas and oceans across the globe, every one crammed with a range of strenuous and energetic investigations. For each, we needed a ship, diving equipment, a great crew and at least three weeks. All of them were filmed for a television series, in which our aim was to seek out the hidden stories of our oceans, to observe some of the oddest inhabitants of the seas and to chart some of the complex and surprising changes that are taking place. And ultimately, to understand better how much we rely on these enigmatic and alien places.

Here's a swift snapshot of what this entailed:

> 'When I was a kid, I wanted gills. Other kids wanted wings – I wanted gills.'

- ‣ More than 1000 dives.
- ‣ More than 700 hours spent under water.
- ‣ Eight expedition ships, which ranged from a beautiful hand-built yacht to a worn-out converted cargo ship and a brilliant Norwegian ice-breaker.
- ‣ One director detained by the authorities.
- ‣ One ship boarded by the authorities several times and impounded once; and numerous bouts of seasickness.

OPPOSITE *The dive team stretch their sea legs in advance of more than 700 hours under the waves.*

Additionally, there were close encounters with African shipwreck-salvage divers, the Eritrean army and any number of bureaucrats from port authorities and government departments. In short, 25 people travelled the world with around 2 tonnes of equipment, which we packed, carried, shipped, assembled, repaired, loved and hated.

The team were already armed with a list of fascinating facts about the oceans:

- The oceans represent over 99 per cent of the living space on earth.
- Earth is the only planet or moon in our solar system that has liquid water on its surface. Ours are the only oceans in the solar system.
- The oceans are continually growing. This is because the rocks on the sea floor are being created anew at the mid-ocean ridge and pulled back into the earth at deep trenches and island arcs. The sea floor is new compared to the continents.
- The highest ocean waves are known to be higher than 30 metres from trough to crest, and occur more often than previously thought. These waves, now being identified by satellite surveillance, are an obvious danger to ships.
- If mined and shared among the world's population, all the gold suspended in the world's sea water would amount to more than 8¾ pounds per person.
- A new species is discovered during almost every deep-sea dive.
- Humans consume 90 million tonnes of animal protein from the ocean every year – the equivalent in weight to more than 900 fully armed aircraft carriers.
- If the thermohaline circulation system ('global conveyor belt') collapsed the Gulf Stream could switch off and Britain might have the same climate as Alaska.
- Oceans house the oldest living creatures on earth. In the 1980s, living stromatolites found in the Bahamas were estimated to be about 2000 years old.
- Our blood is as exactly as salty as the sea.
- If all the oceans were to evaporate, the entire planet would be covered by a layer of salt 50 metres (half a football pitch) thick.
- The average depth of the oceans is about five times the average elevation of the land. The deepest part measures 10,924 metres, in the Marianas Trench near Guam. If the world's highest mountain, Mount Everest, was placed in the trench it would be covered by over 1¼ miles of water.
- The average time a water molecule spends in the oceans is 3200 years.
- Water that sinks in the Arctic will surface 150–250 years later on the equator. The direction of the crucial current that takes it there is changing, due to alterations in the sinking effect in the Arctic.
- The Gulf Stream transports 55 million cubic metres of water per second. This is more than 50 times the flow of all the rivers in the world.
- The weight of all the plankton in the oceans is greater than that of all the dolphins, fish and whales put together.
- Some of the types of plankton that form red tides produce the most potent nerve poison known to man. Depending on the species, they can cause paralysis or trick all the nerves into firing constantly. Other plankton blooms can cause people to lose their memory.

MORE QUESTIONS THAN ANSWERS

OPPOSITE *The dive team took full advantage of their opportunity to dive on some of the world's most beautiful coral reefs.*

OVERLEAF *These maps illustrate the locations of the seven oceans and seas that the team visited and also indicate the routes taken around them.*

But there was much more to discover. The *Oceans* team found underwater caves that preserved the remains of lost civilizations, and wrecks that spoke of ancient battles; they saw rare and endangered creatures that are clinging to survival, and swam with ocean leviathans that dwarf mere humans; they dived in extraordinary, almost alien, marine environments: pitch black waters turned purple by toxic bacteria, and eerie tannin-stained waters that housed bizarre deep-sea creatures. They dived between the edges of the earth's crust to see how oceans are formed and found one of the last remaining places to see the creatures that brought life to the oceans 3.5 billion years ago; rock-like objects called stromatolites that were the first life forms to pump oxygen into the sea and the atmosphere. They dived into a throng of sharks to test out a new shark repellent – and were relieved to find it worked! They observed rarely seen behaviour in sperm whales, and in the Arctic, found a potentially new species of amphipod – a great find as these tiny creatures provide a crucial link in the entire Arctic Ocean food chain.

There were numerous other highlights, including a rare encounter with a green-eyed sixgill shark, a dive alongside Seri Indians using rudimentary gear fashioned from a paint-spray compressor and a beer barrel, and swimming among the terrifying Humboldt squid. They saw thermal vents and underwater volcanoes, dugongs and weedy sea dragons. The dives telescoped the great 'climate conveyers', the oceans currents, into human scale.

The dives telescoped the 'great climate conveyers', the ocean currents, into human scale.

They found evidence of the changes wrought by mankind: warming seas destroying unique ecosystems, overfishing decimating entire species and pollutants triggering a catastrophic invasion of predatory squid. But there were also signs of hope: coral that might harbour a special heat-resistant algae that could also protect the other coral of the world, scientific projects that could restore balance to the seas, and marine creatures that display remarkable abilities to adapt to their changing world. They found out how coral grown in nurseries could replenish damaged reefs. And they were the first to film the fluorescence in Eritrean corals. The phenomenon remains a mystery to scientists who still don't know whether it is part of the coral survival strategy.

The *Oceans* team travelled to nearly all the oceans of the world and several of its seas. And remarkably, each one turned out to have a distinct character, and added its own piece to the enigmatic puzzle that is our marine world.

The salt-lined Mediterranean, with its turbulent straits as well as sun-kissed beaches, is littered with relics from the ancient past, and this trip revealed how the seas have played a crucial role in shaping civilizations.

To N82 W10

Amsterdamøya
Smeerenburg-fjorden

Kongsfjorden

SVALBARD
(NORWAY)

Prins Karls
Forland

Isfjorden

Longyearbyen

Arctic Ocean

Arctic Ocean

Beaufort Sea

Greenland Sea

NORTH AMERICA

Labrador
Sea

North Atlantic
Ocean

North Pacific Ocean

Isla Tiburon

MEXICO

Gulf of Mexico

Guaymas

Punta Concepcion

Sea of
Cortez

Caribbean
Sea

Loreto

SOUTH AMERICA

South
Atlantic
Ocean

Pacific Ocean

Isla Espiritu Santa

La Paz

South
Pacific
Ocean

Grand Bahama

Great Abaco

Bimini

North Atlantic
Ocean

Bazaruto

Andros

MOZAMBIQUE

Great
Exhuma

Lee Stocking
Island

THE BAHAMAS

Inhambane

Indian Ocean

Arctic Ocean

Norwegian
Sea

Barents Sea   Kara Sea   Laptev Sea   East Siberian Sea

Baltic
Sea   Sea of
EUROPE   Okhotsk

Black Sea   Caspian   ASIA
Mediterranean Sea   Sea   Sea of
                                                                                Japan
Red   Yellow
Sea   Sea

AFRICA   Arabian Sea   Bay of   East
                                                   Bengal   China
                                                                                Sea
                                                                                South
                                                                                China Sea

                                                                                Celebes
                                                                                Sea

                                                               Java Sea

Indian Ocean

                                                   Timor Sea

                                    AUSTRALIA

                                                   Tasman Sea

Southern Ocean

ANTARCTIC
                                   Ross Sea

North Pacific
Ocean

Sicily inset

Messina

SICILY
(ITALY)

Ferdinandea   Mediterranean Sea

Lampedusa   Malta

Red Sea inset

Sha'ab Rumi

Port   SAUDI ARABIA
Sudan

SUDAN   Red Sea

                   Dahlak
ERITREA   Archipelago   YEMEN

ETHIOPIA

                              DJIBOUTI

Tanzania inset

Pemba Island

Zanzibar

                    Indian
Dar es Salaam   Ocean

TANZANIA

Mafia
Island

Tasmania inset

St Helens

TASMANIA
(AUSTRALIA)   (via road)

                              Tasman
                              Sea

Hobart   Eagle Hawk
                              Neck

Port Davey

Southern
Ocean

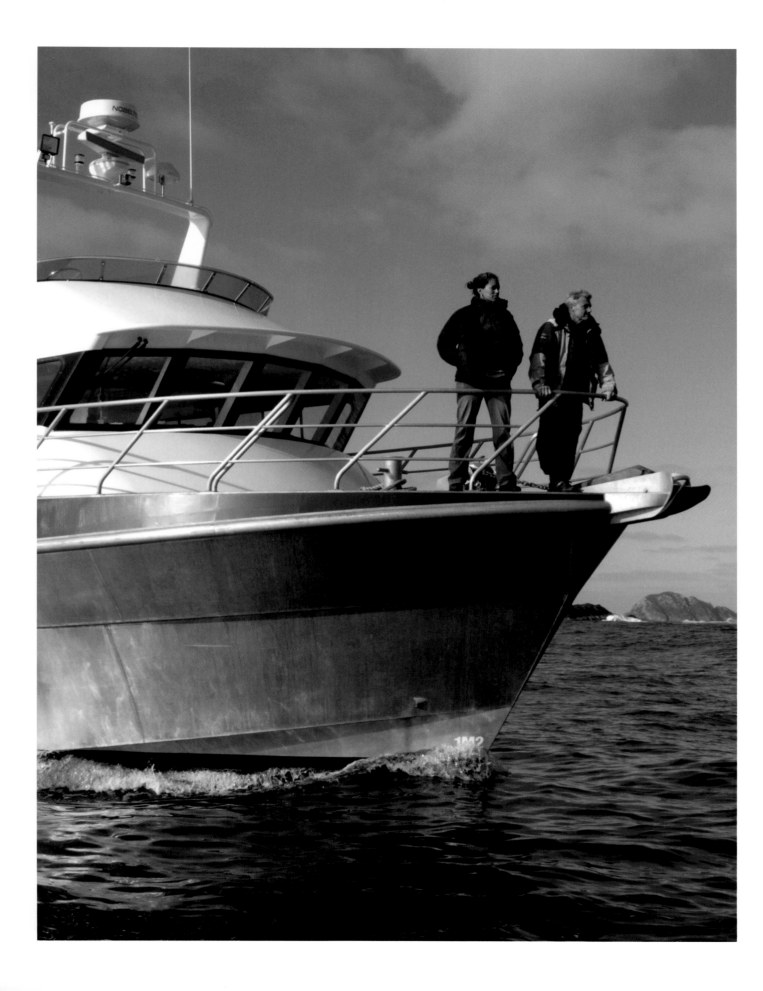

The Sea of Cortez is renowned for its abundant life, especially whales, sharks and dolphins. But it was also the place we discovered the surprising and unpredictable impact of human activity. While overfishing has decimated the population of hammerhead sharks here, the team observed that sea lions were showing signs of successfully adapting to their changing environment.

Measuring the frantic currents of the Indian Ocean could help predict the climate of the future, and the *Oceans* team was on hand to play its part. This mighty sea revealed the immense power of the ocean as we saw how it carves islands and drives cataclysmic storms across the land.

The world's youngest and saltiest ocean, the Red Sea, is one of the most important: it was here that early humans first crossed out of Africa and eventually populated the entire globe. The team found evidence of their first encounters with the sea. In these warm waters the divers sank in leisurely fashion between tectonic plates whose unbidden movement causes deadly earthquakes and tsunamis. And they swam in the slipstream of underwater pioneer Jacques Cousteau, who had set up an experimental underwater village in the Red Sea two generations ago.

The Atlantic is the second largest of all the world's oceans. Despite its size, it was the first to be crossed by boat and by plane and so showed how oceans could be used to bridge cultures and continents. It is also home to the Gulf Stream – one of the most important currents on the planet.

The mysterious Southern Ocean, where the waters of the Atlantic, Indian and Pacific Oceans mingle, is also the biggest carbon sink in the world, and has an elementary effect on weather patterns.

The Arctic is the smallest of the world's four oceans, at just one and a half times the size of the US. And the lowest temperature ever recorded was here, at a bone-chilling minus 68°C. However, the Arctic is the fastest warming region on the planet. Thanks to polar amplification, the effects of global warming are two or even three times greater here. Our dives underneath the polar pack ice revealed the scale and speed of change in the Arctic. In our lifetimes the Arctic Ocean will change so much that it will become unrecognizable to us.

At the end of 12 months the challenge had been embraced. We had evidence, film, photos and eye-witness accounts of some marvels for mankind to share. But, as the divers hauled themselves out of the water for the last time, the overwhelming feeling was not one of relief, or even of a job well done. It was that there were still more questions than answers as far as the world's oceans were concerned. We know more than ever before – but there is still more, much more, to know.

OPPOSITE *Paul Rose and Tooni Mahto survey the scene, on board the* Odalisque *off the coast of Tasmania.*

Measuring the frantic currents of the Indian Ocean could help predict the climate of the future …

CHAPTER ONE

THE MEDITERRANEAN
Cradle of Western Civilization

IN 1961, MARINE GEOLOGIST WILLIAM B. RYAN and senior oceanographer John Brackett Hersey, armed with a newly developed seismic profiler, set out to explore the floor of the Mediterranean Sea. Their trip was long and arduous, made more tiresome by apparently aberrant readings from this newfangled echo sounder. But as they progressed it became clear that these were not, in fact, faulty readings.

Rather than the bedrock they had been expecting to find on the seabed there was, in fact, something entirely different, which accounted for the extraordinary results. Ten years and one deep-sea drilling project later it was finally proved that the seabed was covered by a layer of salt, over 1¼ miles deep.

This discovery was nothing short of astonishing. The layer of salt, nearly as high as the Alps, could only mean one thing – that the meandering Mediterranean Sea, which covered an area of 965,000 square miles and held 1.1million cubic miles of water, must have once completely dried out. As scientists pieced together the geological data, a fascinating story emerged.

THE EARTH MOVES

At some point, about 6 million years ago, the African and European tectonic plates moved together, closing the ring around what was then called the Tethys Ocean. The ocean was landlocked. With no water flowing in from the changes, caused not by the ice ages, but by climatic events (both warm and cold) that caused sea levels to fluctuate.

So here in the Mediterranean we have an intriguing view into the ancient past, when the sea was much shallower than it is today, and when these caves were water-less and high on the shores of the sea rather than deep within it.

This remarkable fact makes sense of some other archaeological findings from the cave systems – fossilized remains discovered just 40 years ago of an endemic prehistoric deer, now extinct. These deer were prolific between 5000 and 6000 years ago.

ABOVE *Stills from video footage of Toomi Mahto and Paul Rose diving in the caves at Cova de sa Gleda. They discovered stalagmites and stalactites formed by the evaporation of drips of calcium-laden water which meant that in the distant past these vast underwater caves must have been dry.*

THE EARLIEST SETTLERS

Perhaps the most exciting finds around these caves are the evidence of early humans. Leading from one cave, Cova Genovesa, to higher ground are the remains of an ancient stone-paved pathway dating from around 2000 years BC. Over a hundred pottery fragments have also been recovered from the cave, dating from the Bronze Age, clear evidence of ancient human settlements on the coast of the Mediterranean.

The caves near Porto Christo have revealed proof of coastal settlers here in Mallorca but there is also evidence of early cultures in other areas of the Mediterranean, including settlements in Lebanon, Palestine, Syria, Anatolia and northern Mesopotamia. Once coastal communities were established, it was the special characteristics of this sea that allowed them to travel and colonize other parts of the Mediterranean. At that time, it was a tiny sea, and almost completely enclosed, which gave it largely calm waters and innocuous tides. This allowed the very early coastal inhabitants to travel throughout the region using rudimentary rafts and boats made of reeds and perhaps even logs. Early man paddled his way across the waters, to places like the Aegean Islands, Sardinia and Sicily, and eventually populated the entire 28,600-mile coastline of the Mediterranean, living by and off the sea. There's a wealth of archaeological evidence to support this Iron Age and Bronze Age diaspora.

For example, caches of obsidian – volcanic glass used in tool-making – dating from around 10,000 years ago were identified on mainland sites in Greece when the only source of this material is the Cycladic island of Milos. Some ancient dwellers of the region obviously liberated it from Milos and took it back to Greece.

Back at Messina, in Sicily, the *Oceans* team is still awaiting the arrival of the expedition boat. The Strait of Messina is one of the busiest shipping lanes in Europe. Every day, liners and transportation ships plough back and forth across this narrow strip of water. But there is still no sign of *Princess Duda*. We have no option but to carry out our planned dives from much smaller launches. It's not a welcome prospect. In all of the relatively calm Mediterranean – this strait is the most dangerous stretch of water.

> In all of the relatively calm Mediterranean this strait is the most dangerous stretch of water.

THE MYSTICAL STRAITS

A restlessly treacherous, funnel-shaped tract of sea severs the island of Sicily from Calabria on the Italian peninsula, at its narrowest point just under 2 miles wide. Here the waters of the Tyrrhenian and Ionian seas seethe, as difficult to navigate today as they were in ancient times.

In the Strait of Messina the tides change every seven hours and the waters flood back and forth through a waterway that is not only narrow but in places just 80 metres deep. Conversely, at other points the depth is as much as 2000 metres. These abrupt topographical changes create the energy that fires up violent swells here. Notorious for whirlpools and strong currents, the dangerous waters of the strait have caused problems for seafarers throughout history and accordingly it became known as the dwelling place of monsters.

In Greek mythology a grotesque six-headed monster named Scylla lived by the cliffs of the Italian peninsula. She would devour sailors if they came within her grasp. On the Sicilian side there was an all-consuming whirlpool called Charybdis which would suck sailors to their deaths. Homer's epic poem the *Odyssey* describes how sailors like Odysseus had to carefully pick out a route between the two menaces in order to survive.

If the strait was not already mythical enough, it is also a known hot spot for Fata Morgana mirages, the same phenomena that sometimes conjure up cities in the Sahara Desert. Fata Morgana mirages are impressive optical illusions, which occur when two layers of air – one hot and rising, the other cooler and descending – meet in the sky. Most people have seen small-scale mirages above a road on a hot day which are essentially refractions of light

28 THE MEDITERRANEAN CRADLE OF WESTERN CIVILIZATION

ABOVE *The port of Messina in Sicily was originally called Zancle, a local word which means 'scythe', and derives from the shape of its natural habour.*

LEFT *The Strait of Messina, which divides Sicily from mainland Italy, is where the waters of the Tyrrhenian and Ionian seas meet. Notorious for their strong currents, these waters have caused problems for seafarers throughout history.*

Modern Monsters of the Deep

The sixgill shark is both primitive and distinctive. Instead of the more advanced five-gill arrangement, which has evolved in most sharks, the sixgill has, unsurprisingly, six gill slits. With six rows of blade-like teeth, white-edged fins and fluorescent eyes it measures up to 5 metres long. The sixgill shark that exists today is virtually unchanged from fossil forms dating back 200 million years.

Very little is known about this shadowy shark, largely because its natural habitat is at extreme depths, say around 2000 metres, so they are inaccessible to humans except those in submarines. There are only two places in the world where it is possible to dive alongside sixgill sharks and one of those is the Strait of Messina where the upwellings force creatures from the sea's abyss nearer to the surface. Even then chances of a sighting remain slender. Only for a few hours between tides at a new moon in spring are the conditions right. Then sixgills may come up to a depth of 40 metres to search for food. Even then, they can move with incredible speed for short periods and this, coupled with a drab brown/grey coloration, makes finding them in the gloom of a skittish current a long shot.

I had already made two exhausting midnight dives and had failed to make contact. I'd followed the local advice, which was to dive in the dark of a new moon, and my diver's sense told me to go for slack water at tide change so that the heaving swell of the strait would be more manageable. To extend my search I decided to dive at 1.30 a.m., the end of slack water. This meant I would travel faster as the dive progressed and therefore cover more ground. I assembled the largest twin diving cylinders I could find and convinced the dive shop to pump them up way over the normal safe working pressure. This would give me about ten more precious minutes under water. Finally, I added a 8¾-pound lump of fresh tuna to my weight belt. Maybe it would attract a shark's attention in a way that I previously couldn't.

It was a relief to head out into the darkness of the strait, getting away from the noise that pervades so many Mediterranean resorts. Everyone needs to be focused before a challenging dive, and extra effort is needed in the strait as the nightclub music, racing motor-cycles and fast cars all blast noise over the water. I felt on the cusp of cultures. The noise of its engine blocking out the sound of disco music, my boat was surging through powerful currents feared since mythological times and below me could be a prehistoric shark.

To leave the boat and feel the water take my weight and that of the heavy dive gear was pure joy, a comfort as I descended through those dim waters into the unknown. As I levelled out at 40 metres I could just make out the shallower parts of the sea bottom as I raced over them in the vice-like grip of the current. After 30 minutes I'd had no luck.

BELOW *The bluntnose sixgill shark, so called because of its distinctive snout, closely resembles fossil sharks from the Triassic period. Little is known about this species as it generally lives at extreme depths, only coming up to the shallows at night to feed.*

Now superior Carthaginian seamanship could be countered by hand-to-hand combat, at which Roman legionaries excelled.

On 10 March 241 BC, a Carthaginian fleet arrived to relieve the Sicilian port of Lilybaeum, modern-day Marsala, which was under siege by the Romans. But their 170 ships were heavily laden with cargo earmarked for their besieged and hungry comrades. The Romans used the element of surprise, and also the newly developed *corvus,* to triumph. In hours, 50 ships of the Carthaginian fleet were sunk and a further 70 captured.

> In hours, 50 ships of the Carthaginian fleet were sunk and a further 70 captured.

In the face of impending disaster, the rest of the Carthaginian fleet fled when a fortuitous change in wind direction allowed them to flee home to Africa. Denied necessary supplies, the Carthaginian army holed up in Sicily had no choice but to surrender. The resulting peace treaty forced Carthage to give up all claims to the island and pay hefty retribution to Rome. It was a decisive victory, with Sicily becoming the first of many Roman provinces, and may have even changed the course of history by substantially altering the regional power balance.

WHAT LIES BENEATH?

Diving almost anywhere in the Mediterranean will reveal fragments that tell of its rich history. But incredibly, off the Egadi Islands and beneath 40 metres of water, lies an eerie reminder of the sea battle won by the Romans against all odds those many centuries ago. Wreckage of Carthaginian ships, decrepit but still decipherable despite the ravages of time and tide, have been found on the sea floor.

The first evidence of a wreck was discovered in 1969 by a British archaeologist, Honor Frost. Investigations revealed that the hastily built ship had been sunk stern-first after being rammed by the Romans. It seems the crew abandoned ship, taking their weapons with them, but there was evidence of the supplies it was carrying, including deer, goats, horses, oxen, pigs and sheep as well as olives, nuts and fruit.

> Among the more surprising finds were traces of cannabis …

Among the more surprising finds were traces of cannabis, which the crew may have chewed as a stimulant before going into battle. Suggestions that the hemp plant could have been used for rope have been rejected as there was already rope aboard, made from something entirely different. Not all the crew escaped. A human skeleton, possibly of a Carthaginian sailor, was found trapped by ballast. When the wreck was judged to be at risk it was taken from the sea to be housed in a maritime museum in Marsala, Sicily.

But in 2004 an even greater horde of riches was unearthed on the same site. Local geologist Leonardo Nocitra discovered the remains of more than 25 warships in shallow graves beneath the sand. He began a search after his nephew spotted the outline of what he believed to be a ship while swimming. Given the risk of divers illegally plundering the site, its exact location has been kept under wraps. But the find is a loud echo from the past, from a sea floor strewn with objects from antiquity.

ABOVE *Near the site of the great sea battle the* Oceans *team found other evidence of human seaborne activity including two anchors: one from a twentieth century vessel and one several hundred years older.*

TREASURES OF THE DEEP

Diving the crystal waters of the Mediterranean provides other clear snapshots of history. Close to the site of the battle of Egadi Islands are two anchors, one clearly from a twentieth century vessel and one much older, possibly early eighteenth century. Just a bit further on is an even older site, one that speaks of the prosperity of the Roman nation after its Punic War victories.

ABOVE *Another fantastic
dive was to examine the
amphorae at close quarters.
This booty, more than
2000 years old, presents
history at its most exciting.
The divers were even able to
make out the name Lazio –
the makers of the wine
carried inside the containers
– carved into the necks of
some of the pieces.*

And it makes for an extraordinary sight. More than 25 metres below the
surface of the Mediterranean lies a mound of amphorae, over 2000 years old.
Each of these ancient containers is 1.2 metres long and covers a sizeable
chunk of the sea floor. The shape of the amphorae reveals their age and where
they came from. They are cylindrical with angular shoulders and long straight
handles, generally oval in section and with a collared rim with a longer, slightly
flared spike. Their technical name is Dressel 1b.

There are around 50 amphorae, and they are the remains of a vast cargo
of over 500, believed to have been carrying Roman wine from southern Italy
in the first century BC – or possibly returning with the amphorae refilled with
a prized cargo of garum. This pungent fish paste, made from rotting mackerel

The Blue-black dive

OPPOSITE *The Oceans team divers investigate the once ferocious but now benign slopes of the volcano of Ferdinandea.*

BELOW *Paul Rose, the Oceans* Expedition Leader *and chief diver.*

I love the feeling of a steaming mug of tea in my hands, especially at sea in the magic moments just before dawn. The boat's rail was crusty with salt, the heaving seas from the night had left a friendly deep ocean swell, no land was in sight and, with some help from my tea, I was once again thinking how much there is to explore in the world. Ferdinandea was just such a place with its chequered, albeit short, history.

I knew the volcano was down there somewhere but, when I headed into the wheelhouse to check our position, our Russian captain said we would have to abandon the dive as he didn't have any AA batteries. Luckily I'd had the tea, so I was awake enough to realize he meant he didn't have any batteries for his GPS.

The Mediterranean volcano of Ferdinandea rises 400 metres from the seabed, to 8 metres from the surface. It is such a huge sea pinnacle that any reasonable navigator

can find it, even with the naked eye. The batteries from my camera made it a certainty. But the trick is getting a good anchorage on such a steep-sided seamount. It's one thing being dragged off the sides of the volcano into safer deep water, quite another to be shipwrecked as you are dragged across the treacherously shallow surface. The area in which Ferdinandea lies is called Terrible Bank on the charts. So we needed to pick our spot carefully. This would have been easier with a breeze as that would have helped us decide which face to go for. As it was, the lazy swell and glassy surface showed no hint of wind so our best bet was to hold position in deep water and dive the volcano summit from one of our small boats.

The dive was beautiful in its simplicity. We descended into that fabulous mid-ocean blue on to a massive black cone. That's it; that's all there was – blue and black. As we got busy measuring the slope angles, collecting lava samples, making temperature readings and taking our photographs I tried to imagine the power of this volcano when it arrived with a head of steam at the surface. It would have been pumping out a massive black smoke plume, and the sea would have been boiling at the newly formed steep black beaches. It must have been an astonishing sight for those sailors back in 1831. And, of course, bemusing to return six months later to find the island had vanished. Formed in the explosion of volcanic ash and mixed with sea water, it remained insubstantial against the force of waves. It simply got washed away, leaving unrequited ambition in its wake.

In contrast to the violence of the geological events and the amusing quirkiness of the political claims, I spent the larger part of the blue-black dive thinking about the rarity of simple surroundings in our lives. It's a setting that attracts me and gives me peace and energy – and I can only get those from deep dives, the polar regions, the sea, in deserts and high in the mountains.

When these volcanoes erupt, the water pressure limits the force of the explosion while the rapid cooling due to the contact with the water creates a vast drop of cooling lava surrounded by a hard crust – called a lava pillow. As lava continues to erupt the pillow breaks open forming secondary pillows, and gradually a solid island structure is formed. This action formed many of the islands that stud the Mediterranean, such as the Aeolian Islands, Stromboli, Pantelleria, Ponza and Santorini.

MEDITERRANEAN UNDER THREAT

The growth of civilization on Mediterranean islands and coasts is today the very thing that threatens the sea. Its shores are home to 150 million people and a further 220 million tourists visit each year. The *Oceans* team is travelling to the north coast of Sicily, west of Palermo, to investigate some of the devastating impact that humans are having on this sea.

As a predominantly landlocked body of water, the Mediterranean has a very low renewal rate and is therefore extremely sensitive to pollution. No less than 80 per cent of urban sewage discharged into the Mediterranean is untreated, and agricultural overspill containing nitrates, phosphates and pesticides adds further contamination. In addition, 600,000 tonnes of crude oil are released into the sea each year from shipping traffic.

... 600,000 tonnes of crude oil are released into the sea each year from shipping traffic.

The effect has been devastating with many species now threatened with extinction. That includes the monk seal, the loggerhead turtle and even a species of seagrass. And, while part of the problem is pollution, another is our insatiable greed.

For over 12,000 years, mankind has lived in harmony with the sea, relying on it as a source of food and livelihood. Now that relationship has crossed the line into relentless exploitation that has disastrous consequences for a number of species. Of the 900 fish species found in the Mediterranean, 100 are fished commercially. Each year, about 1.3 million tonnes of fish are caught worldwide and, although it makes up less than 1 per cent of the world's oceans, the Mediterranean is delivering over 10 per cent of its fish catch.

One of the most devastated populations is the Atlantic blue fin tuna. This magnificent cetacean is the largest tuna, reaching more than 4 metres in length, and weighing more than 1430 pounds. Tuna, especially the blue fin tuna, have been part of Mediterranean culture for millennia. On an island off Sicily, there is a cave painting that dates back to 10,000 BC, of a large fish –

Untreated sewage and crude oil spillages from shipping traffic are causing havoc in the predominantly land-locked waters of the Mediterranean. Seagrass meadows like this (above), which form the basis of a highly diverse and productive ecosystem, found by the Oceans divers is in danger of disappearing due to this adverse human activity. The loggerhead turtle (right) and the monk seal (opposite) are two species also at risk from pollution.

probably a blue fin tuna. The details could not have been drawn by observing the fish while it was in the sea; it must have been landed and it was surely eaten. Pictographs on Egyptian papyrus from 5000 BC show basic fishing techniques while Greek vases from even earlier show fish being cut up in the market. Roman history is redolent with details of trading fish and fish products.

Homer described the fish in the *Odyssey*, which dates from about the eighth century BC, and Aristotle recorded in accurate detail their migration and spawning patterns in 350 BC. The word tuna derives from the Greek word 'to rush'. As they dash around the sea, tuna can reach remarkable speeds, matching cheetahs for pace when they are chasing prey.

For 2500 years they have been a major source of food for Mediterranean people and, for most of that time, there has been no apparent decline in their numbers. But just 30 years ago, that changed. Triggered by the lucrative Japanese sushi and sashimi market, tuna fishing became more intensive. Newly developed purse seines – huge nets that trail behind boats and corral vast numbers of fish – accelerated the catch by 80 per cent.

OVERLEAF *The Strait of Gibraltar – at its narrowest is an 8-mile wide gap between Europe (Spain is on the left) and Africa. At the surface water continually flows eastwards into the Mediterranean from the Atlantic. Outflow from the Mediterranean, which is much more salty, takes place near the seabed, flowing out and down the continental slope, gradually losing its salinity.*

ABOVE *A school of majestic tuna. Blue fin tuna are now endangered and facing commercial and biological extinction.*

OPPOSITE *The Mediterranean has been a source of food for 7000 years as this Greek vase illustrates. Today, intensive fishing is having an alarming effect on its marine life.*

PLIGHT OF THE TUNA

We have come to Sicily's north coast to investigate an even more worrying development – the advent of tuna farms. From the boat, we can see the tops of vast circular pens on the surface of the water, but diving shows the true extent of these sea cages. The pens are 50 metres across and each contains around 300 or 400 tuna. Live tuna have been slowly dragged in vast nets to these pens, where they are fattened up on oily fish for a few months before being sold. For the divers it's a shocking sight. Trapped in the pens, the vast numbers of tuna circle endlessly, very different from their natural behaviour travelling across miles of open sea.

In all there are around 40 such farms in the Mediterranean, each with between six and ten large pens. With a single fish bringing in up to £40,000, it is a lucrative business. But the development of these farms has been catastrophic for the species. The pens contain a high proportion of juveniles who will never reproduce and numbers are dropping fast.

In 2003, the International Commission for the Conservation of Atlantic Tuna was set up in an attempt to control the trade, and set a catch limit of 18,301 tonnes per year. However, conservation groups believe that widespread violations involving quotas that are already twice as high as those advised by scientists have led to a continuing collapse in the blue fin tuna population. Tuna farms in the Mediterranean, for example, have a capacity for nearly twice the quota. Today the blue fin tuna, once celebrated by Homer and Aristotle, is classified as endangered and is facing commercial and biological extinction.

It's a story that is replayed time and again in the Mediterranean and the intensive overfishing is having a dramatic effect on the survival of other marine creatures further up the food chain. Colossal numbers of smaller fish are swept up as by-catch by blue fin tuna fishers and discarded. Without easily available amounts of this prey, larger fish and marine mammals are struggling to survive. Dolphin and sandbar sharks are now under threat while turtles are frequently damaged or killed.

Thirty years ago, when Jacques Cousteau made a series of films in the Mediterranean he was fortunate to find a thriving, varied marine environment, with many species unique to this sea. Today, when his grandson Philippe Cousteau dived with us as part of the *Oceans* expedition he found a barren site, devoid of fish, larger pelagics and the abundant marine life that he'd been expecting. The situation has become so severe that the eastern Mediterranean has now been described as a marine desert.

It's a sobering end to the expedition and reveals a much darker picture of the Mediterranean than the balmy holiday destination most of us know. This is the true Mediterranean. The sea that gave us the roots of Western civilization is now reeling under its impact; and the sea, whose very creation was marked by a mass extinction of sea life, is darkened by the shadow of a similar threat.

> With a single fish bringing in up to £40,000, it is a lucrative business.

vicinity. Inspired by this, scientists set about trying to mimic the chemical that sparks this automatic response. The team has offered to test this newly created repellent on live sharks. If it works, the 'stay away' scent could be incorporated in suntan lotions and wet suits to avoid sharks mistakenly attacking swimmers.

However, first they will test an electromagnetic repellent, made of metal alloys, which could be used to discourage sharks from getting caught on metal longline hooks. This involves catching a harmless juvenile lemon shark and putting it into a state known as tonic immobility. This is a coma-like state induced by simply turning the shark on its back in the water – not something to be tried at home. Everyone is astonished at the impact of this simple manoeuvre. The shark, previously thrashing about to free itself,

ABOVE *Although commercial fishing is decimating some species of shark, many others are killed accidentally, snagged in the longlines and nets of this vast, rapacious industry.*

OPPOSITE *Among the most feared living creatures on earth, sharks have an exaggerated reputation as maneaters. Despite this our divers took a while to get used to being surrounded by adult sharks who showed a marked interest in their human visitors.*

OCEANS

ABOVE *The normal method used to attract sharks is called 'chumming', in which a ball of bait is dangled in the water. It worked wonders when the team wanted specimens on which to try out the chemical repellent.*

becomes still, floppy and utterly unresponsive as soon as it is flipped over. The reason for this behaviour is not fully understood but not even food can wake a shark from this comatose state, giving us a humane way to test the repellent. The electromagnetic repellent is gently brought towards the sensitive electroreceptors on the underside of the shark's snout. The effect is immediate. In an instant the shark wakes up, violently shakes itself free and swims off. The first test is a success.

However, the next test is more dangerous. This time, divers will enter the open sea, surrounded by large sharks, before releasing the chemical repellent in liquid form. The team attracts the sharks in the usual manner – by chumming, that is, by dangling a bait ball in the water. Soon the sea is a boiling mass of sharks in a feeding frenzy. Most are Caribbean reef sharks, but larger tiger sharks have been spotted in the vicinity and are known to come to the research station. Despite the certainty that sharks rarely attack unless provoked, it's a nerve-racking moment as the divers prepare to drop backwards into a sea thronging with large adult sharks, armed only with a prototype repellent.

Under water, the sharks look magnificent, circling the divers smoothly and fluidly. Their wholly hydrodynamic bodies allow a speed and deft man-oeuvrability that is awe-inspiring. Occasionally a large shark approaches to 'nudge' a diver and one even takes a testing nip of a flipper. Sharks sense with their mouths and do this to identify anything new in their environment. As more sharks start to display a marked interest in the divers, it is time to test the repellent. Under water, faced with a 2-metre band of circling sharks, it seems unlikely that a squirt of liquid could stop these creatures focusing on feeding. But, as the repellent disperses, the sharks turn and head away. It's a truly amazing sight to see sharks break off mid-meal in a marked response to the chemical. Within moments the sea is empty. The repellent has been impressive and offers hope that, in time, it may provide a way to build a more harmonious relationship with these mighty beasts of the ocean.

> It's a truly amazing sight to see sharks break off mid-meal in a marked response to the chemical.

PARADISE LOST

When we arrived the Bahamas was certainly living up to its idyllic reputation. The sun was beating down and clear, calm waters lapped against tropical islands. It was easy to forget that these seas are part of one of the most powerful bodies of water in the world. A stark reminder awaited us.

Just days later our boat, *Caribbean Explorer,* pitched and tossed in a huge swell, listing and lurching as the vessel made for a sheltered harbour to sit out the storm. Below decks even the hardiest among the *Oceans* expedi-tion team were groaning in their bunks, watching the vessel roll and tilt in the grip of an Atlantic tempest.

The Atlantic Ocean got its name from one of the Titans of Greek mythology: Atlas. Mentioned by Herodotus in 450 BC, its name means 'Sea of Atlas'. Its scale is vast; it covers a fifth of the earth's surface and is more than six times the size of the US in surface area. It is only outgunned in dimensions by the Pacific. Despite its huge presence, the Atlantic is a relatively young ocean, having formed around 100 million years ago from the break-up of its ancestral supercontinent, Pangaea, from which came the Americas and Africa. The source of the Atlantic's growth is the Mid-Atlantic Ridge, a colossal undersea mountain range, rising 2500 metres from the ocean floor and stretching 10,000 miles from the Arctic to the Southern Ocean. That's four times longer than the Andes, the Rockies and the Himalayas combined.

ABOVE *The calm idyll of a typical Bahamian cay, this is Double-Breasted Cay in the Ragged Island chain, often masks the fact that the sea here is part of one of the most powerful bodies of water in the world.*

It's a powerful ocean renowned for its storms, surging tides and violent winds. The highest tides in the world are found in the Bay of Fundy, which separates New Brunswick from Nova Scotia. During certain times of the year tides can dwarf a three-storey building.

It is dark when *Caribbean Explorer* finally makes it into the lee of an island and the storm shows no signs of abating. Hurricane winds are forecast for the next few days and the unexpected violence of the weather has put the entire expedition in jeopardy.

WILD IS THE WIND

Billowing winds and mountainous waves are the flipside of the picture-postcard Bahamas. That's because there's a lot going on here. The unique geology of this archipelago drives the most powerful and fastest current in the world – the Gulf Stream.

It originates in the Gulf of Mexico but it is in the Bahamas that the Gulf Stream gains its real power. Between the islands of the Bahamas and the coast of Florida the ocean forms a narrow channel, bordered by hard, calcium carbonate rock. As the warm waters come up from the south, the entire output of the Gulf of Mexico is forced through this 60-mile-wide channel. Around 3 billion cubic feet of water per second – that's 15 times the flow of Niagara Falls – is squeezed through the gap. It acts much like a gun barrel, propelling the warm waters out into the rest of the ocean with mighty force and forming the warm Gulf Stream.

With so much power behind it, the stream is driven up the eastern coastlines of the United States and Newfoundland and across 5000 miles of Atlantic Ocean. Once it reaches the middle of the North Atlantic, the current splits in two with the northern stream crossing to Europe. All along the northern route the Gulf Stream water continues to release heat and moisture to the atmosphere, making the climate of the region it passes through warmer and wetter. The amount of heat it holds is prodigious, enough to supply the whole planet's energy needs 100 times over. When it releases heat around the countries of northern Europe it dramatically changes the climate, raising air temperatures by as much as 10 degrees Celsius, and allowing palm trees to grow in western Scotland, at latitudes which otherwise would be frozen for considerable parts of the year.

The southern part of the Gulf Stream hits West Africa and recirculates back to the Caribbean Sea, combining with it to form the North Atlantic subtropical gyre. And this also plays a crucial role, preventing the tropics from overheating by moving warm water away from the equator.

Apart from changing the climate across much of the planet the Gulf Stream also acts as an ocean highway, carrying plant spores, animal larvae and even adult organisms over huge distances. And, as the *Oceans* team discover, it was also a highway for civilizations – bringing people thousands of miles to form settlements in new worlds.

After days of delay, waiting for the storms to pass, there are finally signs that the worst is over. Our goal is to explore this part of the Atlantic, to discovers something of what makes this ocean perhaps the most influential on our planet. The morning dawns clear, and the sea has regained its bright blue sparkle. There is time to marvel at the sheer abundance and variety of sea life.

ABOVE *This NASA QuikSCAT satellite image shows the weather systems and wind patterns at work in the Atlantic Ocean at any given time. The orange circles indicate hurricane force storms; purple indicates medium strength winds while the lighter winds are blue and wind direction is indicated by the white arrows.*

CORAL REEF PREDATORS

Among the fabulous species that throng the Atlantic there are some unwelcome visitors. Recently, a deadly invader has arrived, threatening the natural fish stocks and decimating the ecosystems along the western edge of the ocean. The next mission of the trip is to assess the damage it is wreaking.

The invader is the beautiful but deadly lionfish species. These delicate fish have fins that have been adapted into flamboyant, fan-like structures that are frilled around the edges, making the fish appear much larger than they actually are. But a fragile appearance belies their true nature as these are some of the most poisonous creatures in the sea. Along their backs is a row of spines, loaded with venom. The sting kills many marine creatures instantly and causes humans intense pain, redness and swelling. Indeed, though a lionfish sting is rarely fatal, there are stories of fishermen who would rather drown themselves than suffer the agony of the lionfish barb.

... a fragile appearance belies their true nature as these are some of the most poisonous creatures in the sea.

But the danger posed by the lionfish in the waters around the island of Grand Bahama is not their venom, but the fact that they are here at all. Lionfish are native to the Indo-Pacific Ocean and, outside aquariums, are rarely found elsewhere. In the 1980s a lionfish was spotted in the Atlantic, thousands of miles from its native environment. How it got there was a mystery. The African and American continents act as a barrier to any movement between oceans, and it would be impossible for a tropical animal like the lionfish to swim around the tip of Africa as the water is far too cold. By 1995 there were more sporadic sightings. Perhaps the lionfish had been caught up in ballast as container ships plied their trade across the seas, and dumped as the ship reloaded in the Atlantic, but a more likely suggestion is that a few lionfish were released in Biscayne Bay from a Florida sealife centre which was destroyed by Hurricane Andrew in 1992. Either way, by 2000 lionfish were being spotted in their hundreds, and it is now estimated that there are over a million in the Bahamas alone.

This population explosion is due to two factors. Hundreds of miles from their native sea, they have no natural predators. Also, there's abundant food because their small prey are completely unaware that this new neighbour is a dangerous killer and take no evasive action when the lionfish approaches.

Lionfish are one of the main predators in many coral reefs, active hunters who ambush their prey with outstretched, fan-like pectoral fins. Whole fish, up to three-quarters of their own size, are routinely found in the stomachs of lionfish. On this reef, the divers are astounded by the sheer quantity of lionfish and the seemingly suicidal behaviour of their prey. Lionfish are

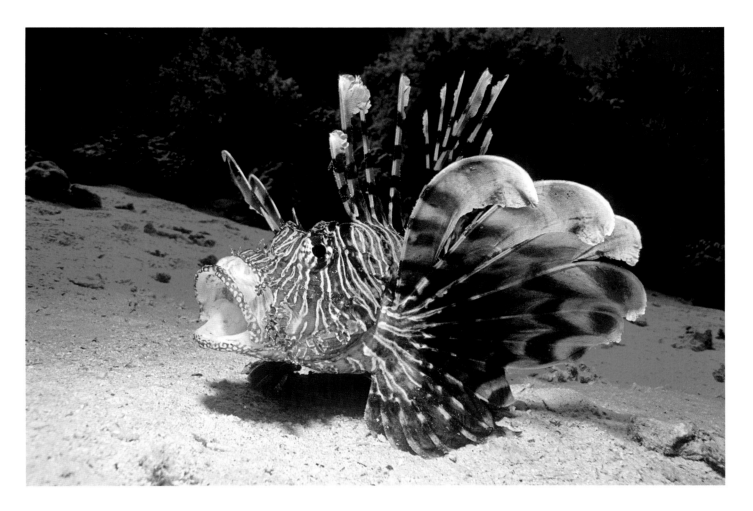

usually nocturnal hunters but in one daytime dive the team witnessed several rare scenes of lionfish hunting and killing prey.

The results are devastating. Lionfish are voracious hunters and, as a result, native populations of reef fish around the east coast of America are being decimated. In this favourable environment, numbers of lionfish are increasing exponentially, helped by their unique reproductive mechanism. They produce floating balls of eggs that can travel vast distances, allowing for greater dispersal. Now, lionfish are found all along the western seaboard of the Atlantic, from the Bahamas up as far as New York.

Difficulties created by invasive species like the lionfish are not restricted to this part of the Atlantic. Worldwide, there is a growing environmental issue as alien species are inadvertently transported into new environments, resulting in the loss of native species and reduction in biological diversity at a rate that ranks only marginally below problems like habitat destruction, a degraded environment or rampant disease.

The divers are in a sombre mood as they gather for dinner that evening, all too aware of how suddenly fragile ecosystems can be tipped into disaster. This area has shown the power and influence of the giant ocean, but has also highlighted the impact that modern life is having on this vital ecosystem.

ABOVE *The beautiful but deadly lionfish are renowned hunters. They only arrived in the Atlantic in the 1980s but are now decimating native populations of the reef fish on which they feed all along the ocean's western seaboard.*

Cave diving

'Oh yeah – you were the guy I gave a hell of hard time to in 1981 because you were so cocky. You thought you were invincible.' So said Wes Skiles, our cave-diving cameraman, as he remembered training me years ago. Luckily I have matured. I am 27 years older and, theoretically, commensurately wiser. And these days Wes is so laid-back that at the start of the cave dive he fell asleep in the water and dropped the camera. We were together again to explore an underwater cave complex with the agenda of trying to understand better how sea levels have changed over time.

Now we stood at the uninviting entrance to Dan's Cave on the island of Abaco. Entrances to flooded caves never look pleasant but still I am drawn to them. This one was a crescent-shaped pool about 4 metres long and a metre wide surrounded by dead trees, poison oak and mud. Bleak though it appeared, it was the only way into about 37 miles of beautiful flooded caves that hold evidence of past sea-level changes.

Tooni, the *Oceans* team marine biologist, and I trust each other and dive well together. And when the dive conditions are challenging we just get better. I was really happy to have Tooni as my buddy on this cave dive as there would be no room for error.

We had stirred up the silt at the entrance so we descended to 20 metres in almost zero visibility. After the halocline (the interface between fresh water and sea water) cleared, visibility was better and we continued down to 25 metres and entered the cave system proper through a cavern that was so big our lights could not reach its end.

I enjoy the thrill of going where most people have never been and of being tested in an extreme environment. There is no room for error in cave diving. The diving skills and techniques that I take for granted when I'm at depth in the big blue or cruising along a colourful reef have to be firmly dialled-in. So it means that from the moment the dive planning and preparation begins I start to enjoy a clear, focused state of mind. And by the time I among the confines of the cave I am so tuned-in to the dive that it seems almost effortless. Short of being an astronaut, cave diving has to be the most exciting way of exploring our planet.

As we moved further into the cave I could see the stalactites and stalagmites that are familiar to all cavers. They can only be formed in air so this proves that these deep caves must have been dry at some point. We swam on through beautifully formed pillars, some in almost impossible shapes. I had to stop a few times just to figure out how they were created. It's in the Bahamas that the theory of underwater cave formations was proved. And it was a great feeling to see them for ourselves.

The dive was a long one and meant we could not ascend directly to the surface. So below the entrance pool we hovered at 6 metres in zero visibility for 16 minutes on a decompression stop to out-gas our nitrogen build-up. Ascending without the stop would have lead to decompression sickness or the 'bends'. Stops like this feel endless. However, the time went quickly as in the ascent to the stop I had been caught in a tree and spent the entire time in complete darkness trying to get out of its tangling limbs.

OPPOSITE *The Bahamian island of Abaco is home to a magnificent underwater cave system and is regarded one of the world's premier destinations for cave divers. The team dived Dan's Cave to see for themselves that these caves had once been dry and were flooded following a rise in sea level.*

Short of being an astronaut, cave diving has to be the most exciting way of exploring our planet.

A LOST CIVILIZATION

ABOVE *This lithograph by M.F. Tobin entitled* First Sight of the New World *depicts Christopher Columbus arriving at the Bahamas in 1492. The exact point of his arrival at these islands is still a matter of debate.*

Throughout the trip, we've come to see just how dependent we are on this vast ocean. It drives our climate, our trade and economies, and it holds our history too. The sea carries stories of our past, preserved for millennia below the waves. Halfway through the expedition we are heading north, hoping to uncover the story of a lost civilization.

About 1000 years ago, the first settlers on the Bahamian islands arrived by boat. The Lucayans had ridden the Gulf Stream's 'express highway' from South America to establish colonies on the islands. Their name derives from the Arawakan Indian words *Lukkunu Kaíri* meaning 'island men'. They share a common ancestry with the Taino societies of Puerto Rico, Haiti, the Dominican Republic, Cuba and Jamaica, from whom they separated in about AD 600 when they began to colonize the Turks and Caicos Islands and the Bahamas. By 1492, when Christopher Columbus arrived in the area, they were living in well-established communities on these islands.

Living primarily off the sea, these peaceful people were skilled potters, carvers and boat-builders. They spun and wove cotton into clothing and hammocks, which they traded with neighbouring communities. The Lucayans, however, had no idea of the wheel, did not use metals for tools, and had no written language.

Religion played a pivotal role in their society. Lucayans worshipped various gods who were thought to control the rain, sun, wind and hurricanes. But their strongest mythology was connected to the ocean. They believed that blue holes – the deep shafts leading to water-filled caves that puncture the islands – had powers of creation. According to legend, the sun, the moon and the Lucayan race came from these sacred caves. And so, when Lucayans died, they were ceremonially returned to them in a ritual burial, through a rock gateway into the afterlife.

The *Oceans* team sailed to Grand Bahama, at the northerly end of the island. It has a number of deep blue holes and the team will dive inside these to look for signs of ancient burial sites. The caves were formed from the erosion of calcium carbonate, which created vast underground caverns rather like giant pieces of Swiss cheese, which became flooded with seawater.

> According to legend, the sun, the moon and the Lucayan race came from these sacred caves.

As the team begin to penetrate one of the caves, it isn't long before another world unfolds. In a vast cathedral cavern beautiful stalactites surrounded by water hang from a ceiling, rather like the vaulted ceiling of an underwater palace. Occasionally, glorious streams of sunlight reach into the depths from openings in the roof of the cave, lighting up the sparkling crystalline rocks. It's a strikingly spiritual place.

We are hoping to find some evidence of the Lucayan burial rituals. Searches like these usually yield only trace evidence, or maybe fragments of artefacts. So the team are absolutely delighted when they discover, nestling deep in a crevice of the cave wall, a human skull. On closer inspection, its forehead appears to be broadly flattened, a strong suggestion that it belonged to a Lucayan. When a Lucayan baby was born its parents would strap a board to the child's forehead so that it grew flatter, in a custom similar to Chinese foot binding. The Lucayans considered a flat forehead a sign of beauty and strength.

> … they discover, nestling deep in a crevice of the cave wall, a human skull.

This flattened skull may have been placed here more than 1000 years ago and, since it was alone rather than in a communal grave, it probably belonged to a tribal dignitary. Up from the crevice there is a narrow opening in the cave roof. Through this the body was probably lowered into the depths of the blue hole. Along with the excitement of the remarkable find, the divers spend a few moments reflecting on the lamentable loss of an entire race.

For these gentle people, idyllic island life was not to last. Spanish gold hunters followed in the wake of Columbus, and began shipping many Lucayans out to work as slaves in the gold mines of Hispaniola. The remainder were forced to dive for pearls. In effect, the Lucayans were worked to death. Those who resisted were killed, while the rest died from European diseases or committed mass suicide. Within a generation the entire Lucayan population of around 50,000 was wiped out, leaving few traces behind it. The Spaniards then sailed away leaving the islands deserted. Now the only testimony to this civilization lies deep in the blue holes, in the grip of the Atlantic Ocean.

THE AIR THAT WE BREATHE

The Atlantic Ocean is home to billions of marine creatures in an array of ecosystems. On the rocks and reefs live colourful sea anemones, sponges and corals. In the shallow waters of the continental shelf, before the seabed drops away to the ocean depths, there is familiar marine life, such as crabs, shrimps and molluscs, as well as many varieties of fish, octopus and squid. Further out in the depths are dolphins, seals and sharks. Faced with this profusion of plant and animal species, it is hard to imagine a time when the oceans were toxic environments almost entirely devoid of life. But they were noxious and inanimate until the era of the stromatolite. This unlikely hero of earth's story looks like a rock but is actually a bacterial city that breathes out oxygen, which eventually sweetened the seas.

This unlikely hero of earth's story looks like a rock but is actually a bacterial city that breathes out oxygen …

Around 550 million years ago stromatolites were the most populous organism in all the oceans of the world. Now there are only two places left on the planet where they can be found: the super-salty waters of Shark Bay in Australia and the tide-scoured channels near Lee Stocking Island in the Bahamas.

The *Caribbean Explorer* sailed for a day before reaching Lee Stocking Island, which sits on one edge of the huge calcium carbonate platform that holds up the Bahamas. Huge drop-offs plunge down the side of the platform to depths of many thousands of metres. As a result, there are large upwellings which make sea conditions particularly treacherous. This is a hostile place with constant wave action and the swirl of ocean debris, and very few organisms can survive. Except, that is, for stromatolites.

At first sight there appears to be nothing in the water except wispy clumps of seagrass and unremarkable lumps of rock. But there's more to these rocks than meets the eye. They are, in fact, composed of thousands of primitive microbes called cyanobacteria which create domed rocky structures – stromatolites. The bacteria live in gooey mats on the top surface of the structures, trapping fine sediments carried across them by tidal currents. The mats are made opaque by the sediments so that the microbes move upwards, seeking sunlight. In this way, layer after layer is cemented to produce cup-like shapes.

ABOVE *Stromatolites are unlikely heroes, but these rock-like organisms produced the oxygen that eventually detoxified the seas and turned them into hospitable habitats for countless marine species.*

From around 2.5 billion years ago, these were the only creatures that could endure the extreme environments found in earth's first oceans. The cyanobacteria are closely related to primitive extremophile bacteria, which can cope with highly toxic chemicals like hydrogen sulphide at close quarters. They also secrete a type of 'sunscreen' on the surface of the stromatolites, which would have protected the microbes from the sun's powerful radiation.

But their greatest legacy to the planet was that as they respire they produce oxygen. From 2.5 billion years ago, stromatolites put oxygen into the seas and the atmosphere. About 550 million years ago oxygen levels reached what they are today. This was enough to both oxygenate the deep ocean and displace the sulphur bacteria, which were previously widespread. The stromatolites transformed the toxic seas into hospitable habitats for millions of species. With a combined photosynthetic activity greater than the world's rainforest canopy, they are the reason for our oxygen-rich atmosphere.

New organisms evolved that used oxygen as a source of energy. These 'oxygen-loving' organisms began to dominate the oxygen-rich seas, and gradually evolved into myriad forms of marine life. Fossil stromatolites have been found in sedimentary rocks of all continents. They have been an important focus for palaeoecologists – those who study the early evolution of life – while other scientists use fossil stromatolites to reconstruct ancient physical environments. For these studies, observations of modern 'living' stromatolites are crucially important for a proper interpretation of the ancient fossils.

Thanks to the humble stromatolite the Atlantic is now one of the world's most productive seas. The most fertile areas for fishing include the Grand Banks off Newfoundland, the shelf area off Nova Scotia, the Bahama Banks, and Dogger Bank in the North Sea, and the major species of fish caught commercially are cod, haddock, hake, herring and mackerel. The ocean is hugely influential commercially. Besides its major transportation and communication routes, it also offers abundant petroleum deposits in the sedimentary rocks of the continental shelves.

THE BLACK HOLE

Without the stromatolite none of this is likely to have occurred. But what was it like in the years before the advent of the stromatolite? Bizarrely, there is one place where you can still experience an ancient, alien ocean. The team is about to head to the island of Andros, south of Grand Bahama and north of Cuba, for possibly one of the most memorable dives ever undertaken.

… there is one place where you can still experience an ancient, alien ocean … the Black Hole at Andros.

The team plans to investigate a remarkable phenomenon. The Black Hole is a perfectly round sinkhole that plunges 47 metres into the soluble limestone – the sedimentary rock that makes up the Bahamas archipelago. Isolated from the rest of the ocean it is an eerie and unique marine environment. But it is the life forms in this sinkhole that make it such an extraordinary place.

The Black Hole was first seen in 1985 by veteran cave diver Rob Palmer. His initial thought was that it was formed by meteor impact, due to its perfectly round shape. But it is now thought that the hole formed from the surface downwards. Puddles of rainwater gathered on the surface and gradually became deeper, to be colonized by bacteria that produced acid as a waste product of their carbon metabolism. This acid dissolved the limestone, leaving a perfect circle, which over time and after the action of many billions of bacteria, has grown to nearly 50 metres deep. From the surface it is an uncanny sight; the still waters appear pitch black and distinctly ominous.

Hardly anything is known about the microscopic animals in the Black Hole, and only one research team has ever dived it before. Our team plans to descend into the acidic depths, taking probes to measure temperature and oxygen levels.

The dive of a lifetime

I should have seen it coming – you can't travel back in time 3.5 billion years without being flippin' uncomfortable.

My first sight of the Black Hole from the helicopter brought the familiar feelings of excitement and anticipation. I love those moments. Part of me is just bursting to get to it while a voice in my head is working out risks and how to manage them. The Black Hole on Andros Island is a one-off. Nothing like it exists anywhere else on earth. That alone makes it a great diving expedition. I'd heard that the hole was about 50 metres deep with a strange layer at about 18 metres that keeps the top and bottom waters isolated. We planned to dive through this layer and see what happened on the other side.

From the start it was clear this was going to be a stretch. The site is only accessible by helicopter. The area around the hole is a cross between Yorkshire limestone karst scenery, a mangrove swamp and a nightmare tangle of poisonwood. The rock edge of the hole has formed into a brittle honeycomb with razor-sharp edges.

The first part of the dive felt like many freshwater dives – cool, clear, green-tinted water with us cruising down a steep rock on the descent. We soon lost sight of the wall and then, as expected, we came on to the top of a dense brown layer that looked exactly like a muddy bottom. It moved in thick clouds. We slowed to study it and immediately felt the water get hot. Not pleasantly warm, but unhealthy-get-out-of-there hot. Within a few seconds visibility went to zero. The only way I knew my torch was on was to hold it against my mask. I held the front of the camera and pulled it to my mask so that I could describe the experience and keep us all together.

I was almost overwhelmed by a sudden blast of the smell of rotten eggs, which made no sense. You usually can't smell anything under water as your nose is inside the mask.

In this case I could smell the bacteria because the chemicals were absorbed into my skin and I smelled them through my sinuses. I was being permeated with chemicals. I kept reminding myself that this layer was made of hydrogen sulphide but I couldn't remember the level of toxicity. My overwhelming feeling was that I just had to go deeper.

In a few seconds we entered an even smellier layer that was blood red – almost purple. I did not want to hang around here but was drawn into experiencing it for as long as possible. We continued our descent and, at 22 metres, finally made it through to clear, completely black water which was reassuringly familiar – just like a normal night or cave dive. That was until I looked up. The 'ceiling' was black with bright green holes, where we had come through it, surrounded by the strange red-purple layer underneath.

> … the chemicals were absorbed into my skin … I was being permeated with chemicals.

I realized that the water we were exploring was what all of our seas were like 3.5 billion years ago. The black water with its dead feeling is a long way from the beautiful oxygen-rich, life-giving oceans we have now.

There was no avoiding it. We had to go back up through the layer and I needed to experience it again just to check that I was right about the assault on my senses. Sure enough, the visibility went to zero in the red-purple, smelly super-hot layer, which was followed by the green smelly layer and then the wonderful cool, clear life-giving fresh water. I raised my arms in joyous triumph as we enjoyed the slow ascent in clean water.

I felt a bit odd after the dive and I spotted John, our safety diver, throwing up in the weeds. Tooni had a headache and Mike, the cameraman, had a sore throat. It wasn't until late that evening that we all began to feel good again. There are even some longer-term effects – my hair has gone a weird colour. Was it worth it? You bet. It was a dive of a lifetime that took us back to what the sea was like 3.5 billion years ago.

The sudden temperature spike at around 18 metres, obvious to the divers even through their wet suits, occurred as they entered a metre-thick layer of bacteria. But that wasn't the only oddity. Suddenly the water turned a bright, almost psychedelic red-purple. The layer of microbes is so dense that it absorbs nearly all the sunlight entering the hole. By reflecting only a small amount of the longer wavelengths, the microbes cause the intense red-purple colour. This is what makes the hole appear black on the surface. The bacteria here are so dense that they would weigh about 5 tonnes if they were dried out. They are able to photosynthesize using sunlight to produce energy. However, the water deep inside the Black Hole has virtually no oxygen dissolved in it, which is vital for photosynthesis to happen. So, the bacteria have evolved an ingenious way to harness the sun's energy by using sulphur in place of oxygen and producing acidic hydrogen sulphide as a waste product. In high concentrations, hydrogen sulphide is toxic and the concentrations produced here are overwhelming. The characteristic 'rotten egg' smell of the sulphurous by-product is so intense that not only could the divers 'smell' it through their skin, but on the surface, too, the stench was unmistakable as their air bubbles carried the gas up to the surface. As the divers stayed in the layer, the toxic acidic gas started to irritate their skin, causing stinging, itching sensations. This was potentially dangerous and the surface safety team monitored the situation carefully.

> ## Suddenly the water turned a bright, almost psychedelic red-purple.

Still, the divers were determined to see what was beyond the bacterial layer so they descended even further. Under the layer the team were in the pitch black. They shone a torch up on to the underside of the microbial blanket to see globules of bacteria raining down on them. The temperature also dropped dramatically when they moved out of the sulphur-bacteria layer above, rather like being plunged into a cold-water pool. This is because no sunlight can penetrate through the bacteria mat, so the lower lying bacteria adapt to this by using the heat energy from chemicals in the water instead of the sun. The readings confirmed that the water is completely devoid of oxygen.

The environment inside the Black Hole is as hostile as it gets. With no oxygen or sunlight, very little life can thrive. And this is what our planet's oceans would have been like when they first formed around 3.5 billion years ago. From around 3.5 billion to 2.5 billion years ago the earth's atmosphere was oxygen-deficient. Although some photosynthesizing bacteria were producing oxygen, volcanic gases were reacting with it so quickly that very little accumulated in the atmosphere.

> ## The environment inside the Black Hole is as hostile as it gets.

Sulphur began to gather in the ocean and, in this oxygen-free sulphur environment, only oxygen-intolerant sulphur-bacteria could survive, much like the bacteria found in the Black Hole. By diving in this unique place the *Oceans* team dived back in time to discover what might have lived in our oceans when they first formed. Now they know it to have been a toxic, black, virtually lifeless void, colonized by nothing except patchy mats of red-purple bacteria.

Despite the thousands of dives they have accrued between them, none of the divers had ever seen a marine environment like this anywhere else in the world. This was a hazardous dive, and we retrieved the divers earlier than planned because of safety fears. But even so this unique dive came at a price. After prolonged exposure to the toxic chemicals, one diver was severely ill, brass fittings on the dive equipment had become tarnished and the hair of the team leader had turned an odd shade of gold.

In the dying light of a tropical sunset, sipping beer and mojitos, the team reflected on what has turned out to be an unforgettable trip. For the British and the American on the boat the Atlantic is the most familiar of all the world's oceans, and one that is easily taken for granted. But even in this relatively small corner, we have witnessed the potency and influence of this mighty ocean.

The storms that dogged the beginning of the expedition, and the massive power of the Gulf Stream, speak of the Atlantic's crucial importance in shaping the world's weather and climate. Its trade routes, fisheries and natural reserves have made it a giant in world commerce, and as a highway linking continents and peoples it has played a major role in shaping our history. As the sun slips below the horizon of this mighty, vast sea, it feels appropriately named – as a Titan.

ABOVE *In stark contrast to the Black Hole the Bahamas are also home to a number of Blue Holes. These water-filled caves – found both on land and offshore – were formed during several ice ages but unlike the Black Hole are filled with regular sea water. Diving here is much more pleasant and they are a major attraction for divers in search of rarely seen tropical marine environments.*

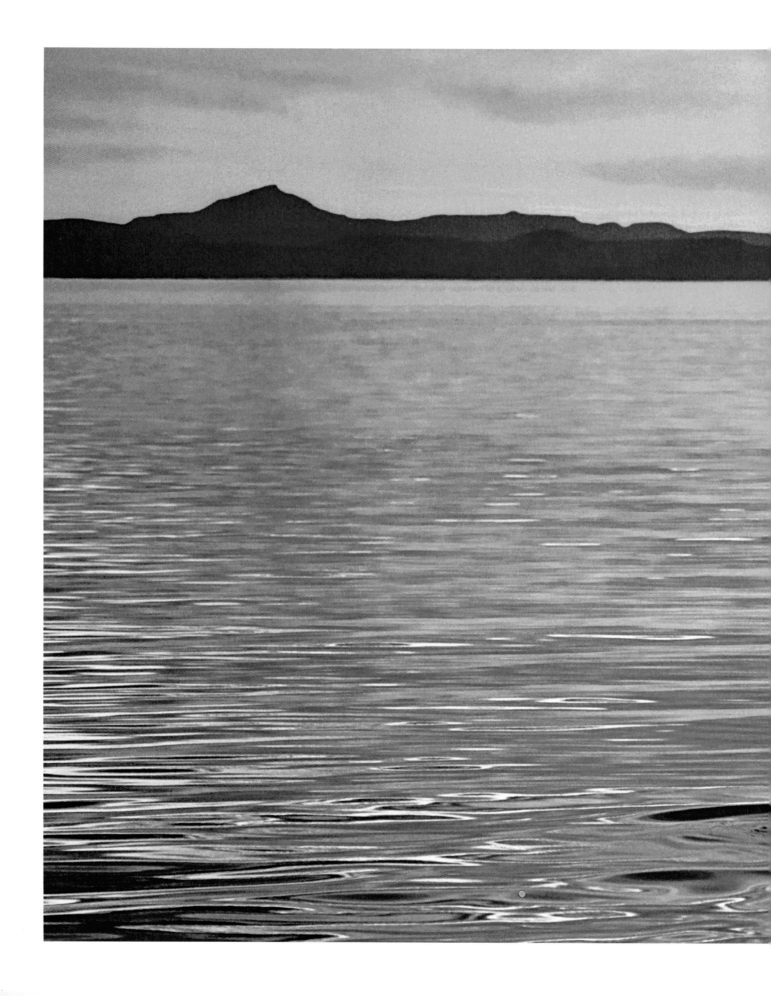

rather confusingly, as the 'black turtle'. Other visitors include whales and whale sharks, pods of dolphins and elephant seals. The California gray whale completes the longest migration of any mammal by spending a few winter weeks each year in breeding grounds here before returning to the Bering Sea 5000 miles away. More species of whales and dolphins feed and breed in the Sea of Cortez than in any other part of the world. Overall, nearly 900 fish species and 34 species of marine mammals swim these waters, and more than 800 of the sea's marine and coastal species are found nowhere else in the world.

OPPOSITE *Whale sharks are migratory visitors here, usually in September or October, to feed and breed. They are often accompanied by ramora, or sucker fish, who hitch rides on these gentle giants and keep them clean of parasites.*

THE SHARK AND THE SNAIL

And right at the top of the food chain, the apex predators, are the sharks. At least, that's how the script always used to read. But that's old news today. For the last 20 years or so the most deadly killers have been mankind and it is sharks who have all too often been the prey.

Man had fished the waters here for centuries, with few far-reaching effects. Then came the era of commercial fishing, with gill nets and then drift nets scooping up everything small and enormous from this diverse habitat. Sharks were frequently the victims of the tuna fishermen.

But then the demand for shark fin soup in the increasingly wealthy Far East put a different complexion on the issue. When a fin weighing just over 2 pounds can fetch between $50 and $100, it comes as no surprise to learn that commercial shark fishing has become so intensive. The practice of slicing off the fins and throwing the shark back is illegal in Europe and the United States. Although it is not illegal in Mexico it is heavily discouraged, but we saw signs that it is still happening here. It's impossible to say just how many sharks are killed worldwide. One estimate out of Hong Kong, where many of the fins are landed, says the number is between 26 million and 73 million each year; others suggest it is over 100 million.

For the last 20 years or so the most deadly killers have been mankind …

By the time the Sea of Cortez was added to the UNESCO list of World Heritage Sites in 2005 it was already sorely depleted of its fish and marine mammal populations. The next mission for the *Oceans* expedition team is to investigate how critically overfishing and the ravaged fish stocks have affected the scalloped hammerhead shark.

There are nine species of hammerheads, so called because the long, flattened lobes projecting from the sides of their heads resemble a flattened hammer. The 'hammer' is, in fact, a highly complex organ containing both olfactory organs and highly developed electroreceptors. The nostrils are located near the outermost tips of the hammer and have specialized grooves that channel scent-bearing water to the nostrils. By having their nostrils mounted far apart, hammerheads may be able to sample a wider portion of the water column giving them increased acuity – a kind of 'stereo sniffing'. Hammerheads are often the first sharks to arrive at an area where fish offal is being dumped overboard, suggesting that their sense of smell is particularly well developed. Question marks still exist about hammerhead behaviour as they are notoriously tricky to observe.

... they can even locate prey buried under the silt of the sea floor.

The hammer also houses the specialized electroreceptor, called 'ampullae of Lorenzini'; the ampullae are distributed over the entire undersurface of the hammer and are acutely sensitive to electromagnetic fields, including the weak bioelectric aura that surrounds every living creature. Hammerheads often swim very close to the seabed, swinging their strange T-bar heads in broad arcs to sense this minute electrical field. Using this mysterious sense they can even locate prey buried under the silt of the sea floor.

It's this electromagnetic sense that draws them to the Sea of Cortez. Thanks to its volcanic past, the sea is dotted with large seamounts; undersea mountains typically formed from volcanic rock, mainly basalt. This basalt is rich in magnetite (ferrous-ferric oxide), the most magnetized of all naturally

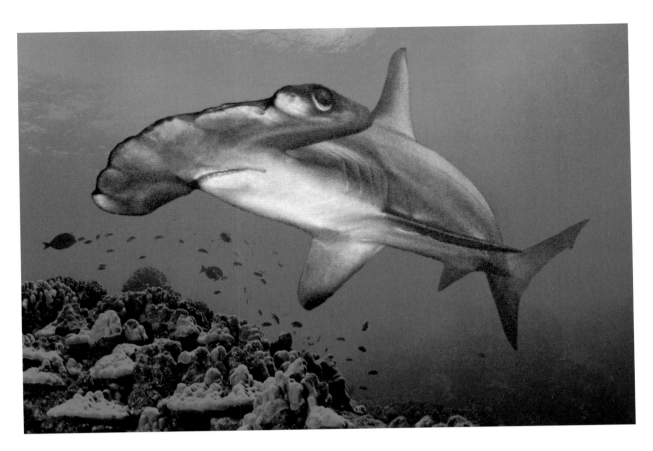

occurring minerals, so seamounts emit a strong magnetic field. Traditionally, seamounts have been a rich source of food for sea life. The hammerheads' sensors can detect minute changes in magnetic polarities, enabling them to find seamounts from many miles away. As a hammerhead swims it moves its head from side to side, scanning the water for a signal. It's like a shark GPS system, mapping the ocean highway.

Just decades ago, huge schools or 'shivers' of hammerheads would congregate around these large seamounts, drawn by both the magnetic field and the array of fish found here. Hammerheads are one of the few species of shark known to congregate like this, and they do so solely during the daytime. At night they disperse in order to hunt. One suggestion is that the hammerheads use the magnetic dipole of the seamount as a navigational tool, a landmark on their migration route northwards through the Sea of Cortez. Whatever the reason, the mounts in the Sea of Cortez have always been one of the places in the world to see vast shivers of hammerheads, numbering up to 500 sharks in a group.

The *Oceans* team is planning to investigate the current health of the population by diving at a particular seamount known as a hammerhead congregation point. Technically it is a complex dive. El Bajo seamount lies 40 metres below the surface and, because hammerheads are frightened off by the air bubbles of normal scuba gear, the dive will have to be done with silent, bubble-free re-breathers.

ABOVE *The population of scalloped hammerhead sharks in this area has been seriously depleted in the last 30 years due to overfishing.*

OPPOSITE *In the past huge schools or 'shivers' of hammerheads would congregate around the large seamounts of the Sea of Cortez. However, these are now rare as this fascinating species is fast disappearing from these waters.*

Re-breathers

My career as a diver spans 40 years and during that time I have wasted most of my air. This is not because I wasn't working or having fun under water, but because for almost all of my dives I have used SCUBA equipment – Self Contained Underwater Breathing Apparatus. This is the kit invented in 1942 by Emile Cagnan and Jacques Cousteau that involved divers carrying high-pressure cylinders of air on their backs. You can easily spot scuba divers in the water because of the stream of exhaust bubbles that follow them and when you are using scuba gear it's hard to get really close to the fish because of these noisy bubbles. The instant you exhale, the fish dart away. And that's not all – most of the precious air in the diving cylinder is wasted in the bubbles.

Scuba gear is what most divers use these days – it's pretty simple to use and maintain, is safe and reliable, and just about everyone uses it when learning to dive. But if you want to get really close to marine creatures, spend hours under water, engage in underwater warfare or live in space, then you need a CCR – Closed Circuit Re-breather unit. That's because, unlike scuba divers with their tell-tale bubble trails, CCR divers emit no bubbles at all – so it's a completely silent and incredibly efficient way to dive. It works by allowing the diver to reuse his or her exhaled air by scrubbing it clean of carbon dioxide and adding small amounts of oxygen. Divers using CCR still carry cylinders, but they last a great deal longer and instead of a diver's time under water being measured in minutes, it can now be measured in hours.

And there are also other benefits in using a CCR unit. Because it gives you a perfect breathing gas for your depth there is much less chance of getting either nitrogen narcosis – high-pressure nitrogen affecting the brain and giving deep divers a dangerous semi-drunken/high feeling – or decompression sickness, when high-pressure nitrogen is absorbed into the body on long, deep dives resulting in joint and nerve damage, aka 'the bends'.

So if you want to dive long, deep and silently you should always opt for a CCR. It's worth mentioning that it takes some getting used to. It's not surprising; after all, how many pieces of equipment do you have that come off the shelf ready to use at depths of down to 100 metres, or have instructions that say, 'Warning. This equipment can kill you without warning'?

ABOVE SCUBA *co-inventor Jacques Cousteau (top), and Paul Rose with a* CCR *unit.*

OPPOSITE *Scuba's tell-tale bubble trail.*

The currents make this water murky. Visibility was only about 2 metres, so I followed the diver's garden hose from the surface and swam down until I bumped into him. His work rate was staggering. He ran along the bottom until he found scallops, then knelt, yanked them out with his metal hook, stuffed them in his bag and ran on again at an amazing pace.

He works for about two hours, down to 25 metres deep, twice a day, every day of the year. If you put those figures into a dive computer or a dive table you'll soon see that this man will have decompression sickness – the bends – not to mention the effects of breathing air from his old paint-sprayer compressor, the oil from which will probably coat his lungs with an irreversible layer of fine oil that is highly likely to lead to lipoid pneumonia. One good thing; he now has a filter for his air so he doesn't breathe in impurities like dust and sand any more.

The name by which the Seri are known, *Kumkaak*, means 'the people'. These nomadic hunter-gatherers of Mexico, renowned for extraordinary endurance, are one of the few indigenous people who have never been conquered by invaders. Conquistadors, Jesuit priests, the Mexican government and entrepreneurs were met with varying degrees of ferocity. Now only about 420 Seri remain, down from about 5000 in the seventeenth century and 2000 in the 1890s. This is the result of imported diseases rather than warfare.

The effective removal of all fish in the sea forced the Seri to find new money-making ventures. They made craft goods for the tourism industry, which meant moving off their ancestral land of Tiburon Island – which became a game reserve in 1965 – to camps on the mainland. Granted exclusive fishing rights to the scallops in the area by the Mexican government in 1970, they earn income by selling access rights.

The Seri regard the leatherback turtle as a sacred embodiment of their ancestors. Traditionally, if one was inadvertently captured they held a four-day ceremony to protect it, building a shelter, painting powerful motifs on its back, and singing and dancing. One ceremony took place in 2005, but no others had occurred for about 20 years, because leatherback turtles are now rarely found in the northern Sea of Cortez – they are one of the world's most endangered marine turtles.

They are one of the few indigenous people in Mexico who have never been conquered by invaders.

RIGHT *The leatherback turtle, regarded by the Seri as a sacred embodiment of their ancestors, is one of the world's most endangered species of marine turtle.*

ARRIVAL OF THE EUROPEANS

Sea Escape heads north. The sea is flat, the sunset golden. The cacophony of seabirds has ceased and peace is settling like a blanket as the night falls. Only the insistent roar of the generator breaks the stillness of the evening.

Humanity has enjoyed a complex relationship with the Sea of Cortez. From earliest times, people have lived along these shores, using the marine riches as a source of food and livelihood. Indigenous people lived in harmony with the sea, seeing themselves not as exploiters of its harvest, but as its custodians. Today, only one of these indigenous communities survives – the Seri Indians.

For the Seri Indians, the key to their relationship with the sea was stewardship. It housed the spirits of their ancestors and was a sacred place to be nurtured and sustained. That respectful relationship was blown apart when Europeans discovered this narrow sea in the sixteenth century.

The Spanish conquistador Hernan Cortez (1485–1547), for whom the sea is named, accidentally came across it while exploring the Mexican coast of the Pacific Ocean in 1536. At the time Cortez was stung by perceived insults from the Spanish monarchy, hungry for more than the Aztec Empire that he had already claimed in their name. But his experiences in Baja California fired his enthusiasm for exploration once more. He returned to Europe with tales of untold riches – pearls by the handful that could be simply lifted off the seabed.

> Soon, another rich commodity was discovered – a prize worth more than gold itself.

Trading routes were quickly established, and thousands of galleons plied the Manila route between Europe and the Sea of Cortez. Soon, another rich commodity was discovered – a prize worth more than gold itself. Its lyrical name is guano but it's otherwise known as bird or bat droppings. With its abundant marine life, the Sea of Cortez was a magnet for seabirds like the blue-footed booby, frigate birds, the brown pelican, egret and ten different species of gulls, and the many islands that dotted the sea were covered in guano, baked in the dry sun and built up over thousands of years to layers 30 metres deep. Guano is rich in phosphorus and nitrogen. At the time it was valued both for fertilizer and in the manufacture of gunpowder.

In the nineteenth century this unlikely commodity was rediscovered as a powerful economic lever. Indeed, guano was so effective at increasing crop yields that demand went through the roof. Europeans raced here to mine the smelly, white-capped islands in the sea. The most isolated of the islands, San Pedro Martir, even became a penal colony, with the prisoners sentenced to gather guano. The trade brought industry where none existed. It expanded empires, made companies rich and exploited both the local population and the marine environment of this tiny sea. The traditional approach of the Seri Indians, as custodians of this rich resource, was lost in the face of commercial imperatives.

Today, the complex ecosystems in the Sea of Cortez are in constant flux as human activity impacts on every aspect of the rich sea life. Pollution from agrochemicals and urban waste is threatening the coastal marine habitats, and 39 marine species in the sea are classified as endangered or threatened.

As we've already established, overfishing is rife and it's not limited to sharks such as the hammerhead. Shrimp, snapper, tuna, grouper, sea bass, marlin and sardines are all being devastated by the vast fishing industry here. For every pound of shrimp netted, another 10 pounds of marine species are killed then simply discarded.

The fishing industry is triggering one of the most dramatic changes in the balance of sea life here. As numbers of the larger, vertebrate fish fall, there are fewer predators to keep the invertebrate species in check. Now, in several of the world's oceans, the invertebrates are taking over, becoming the dominant species. It's the invasion of the ctenopods, invertebrate marine creatures such as jellyfish, squid and octopus. And nowhere is this more extreme than here in the Sea of Cortez.

ABOVE *Tiburon Island (tiburon is Spanish for shark) is the largest island in the Gulf of California. Once the ancestral home of the Seri Indians it is now a nature reserve. The island, home to a huge community of seabirds, is still covered in guano, once a valuable commodity used both for fertilizer and gunpowder.*

THE INVASION OF THE CTENOPODS

Sea Escape reached Loreto, halfway up the sea, to survey the main site of the invasion but, in the morning light, there was little evidence of it. However, as night falls, the sea transforms. Instead of calm, clear waters, the sea is alive with literally hundreds of huge, voracious Humboldt squid. They take their name from the Humboldt current which runs through the east Pacific Ocean, but they are also known as jumbo squid or, among the local fishermen who fear them, *diablos rojos* – red devils.

The Humboldt is the Terminator of the squid world.

The Humboldt is the Terminator of the squid world. The squid can reach up to 2 metres long and weigh 99 pounds. The huge head, or mantle, is surrounded with feeding tentacles, each one studded with suckers for grasping prey. Each sucker contains sharp barbs, which the squid uses to pierce the flesh of prey and drag it to its mouth. These squid are aggressive hunters and, although their main diet is small fish, they have been known to attack sharks, each other and even, so they say, local fishermen, trapping them in their powerful tentacles and ripping them with their barbed suckers.

OPPOSITE AND LEFT
Humboldt squid, which grow up to 2 metres long, are known to local fisherman as diablos rojos – *red devils. They have barbed suckers on their tentacles which pierce the flesh of their prey. These aggressive creatures have been known to attack sharks and even fishermen.*

Swimming at speed the Humboldt could match the coyotes that roam the nearby deserts. They have even been known to fly. In a bid to hunt food or escape predators they are able to propel themselves out of the waves by expelling water from their bodies.

And there's evidence that they are becoming more cunning. Recent research suggests that the Humboldt are communicating with each other and hunting in packs. All squid can emit light and the Humboldt change colour rapidly from maroon to ivory and all shades in between, the colours pulsing like a strobe. The variation and changes in frequency of the pulses strongly suggest that this is a form of communication. As the squid pulse at each other, they seem to be working co-operatively as a pack, to herd and trap shoals of prey.

During the day they maintain depths of at least 70 metres, making research and any observation of their behaviour all but impossible. Only at night do they rise near to the surface, and then they are at their most intimidating. Elusive, perhaps, but not rare as they arrive in great numbers and are hungry for flesh.

> Recent research suggests that the Humboldt are communicating ... and hunting in packs.

In the waters off Santa Rosalia, Humboldt packs can reach as many as 1000 individuals, a churning mass of voracious hunters. Yet just a few decades ago, there were no squid at all here.

When John Steinbeck and biologist W. Ricketts travelled here in 1940, documenting the abundant marine life, their log contained no mention of any squid. At the time Humboldt squid were confined to more southerly waters off Peru in South America and it was only 20 years later, in 1959, that they were first scientifically identified in the Sea of Cortez – and then merely as an occasional, rare species in this territory. In fact, right up until the late 1970s, Humboldt squid were rarely seen in the sea.

Now, there are estimated to be over ten million squid in the Santa Rosalia area alone, within an area of just 25 square miles. The explosion in their numbers is driven by several factors. The steep decline of the squid's natural predators through overfishing is certainly one cause, but the increase in ocean temperatures as a result of global warming may also play a part, by allowing the squid to survive further north.

Whatever triggered the invasion, it is now growing exponentially. Squid fishing has become a prime industry in the area, with hundreds of fishing pangas going out every night and simply pulling the squid out of the water. In one night, a single boat can catch over 2000 pounds of squid and every year over 100,000 metric tonnes are landed from the Sea of Cortez. None of this seems to be stopping the inexorable increase in squid numbers. Squid only live for a year or so, but they have a vast reproductive output. In her short lifetime, each female produces 30 million eggs. The Humboldt squid is now a dominant species in the Sea of Cortez and numbers are still climbing.

At 3 a.m., after several night dives in rough seas, with the constant threat of attack from the squid, it's hard to feel admiration for these aggressive creatures. And yet, their survival is a triumph. They are the most successful of all the marine life here and species of squid are beginning to repeat this pattern in seas all over the world.

> In her short lifetime, each female produces 30 million eggs.

LIONS OF THE SEA

Exhausted and battered by the strong swell, there is only one thing keeping the *Oceans* expedition team going, and that is the thought of the final mission of the trip: to see sperm whales. Some of the largest animals on the planet, sperm whales in the Sea of Cortez are among the few winners in the ecological roulette played out here. A few years ago, these giants of the ocean

DANCE OF THE LEVIATHANS

Finally *Sea Escape* arrives at San Pedro Martir. The island looks spectacular, its white-capped rocks sparkling in the sun giving it an ethereal appearance quite at odds with the distinctly earthy stench of the guano that creates the glistening white mantle.

This is one of the best places in the world to see sperm whales, as it's a popular breeding ground and resting place on their long migration across the oceans. Some female sperm whales have been tracked here from the Galapagos Islands, a journey of over 2360 miles. In fact, the Sea of Cortez attracts a vast diversity of whales: fin whales, blue whales, pilot whales, killer whales, humpback whales and great whales are all found here. Congregations of so many huge mammals make the rich, fertile protected waters of the Sea of Cortez unique.

Although sperm whales are drawn here and the populations are stabilizing, even so sightings are rare and relatively little is known about these majestic creatures. The *Oceans* team hopes to find surface spots and to check on the health of the population, adding significantly to the relatively small amount of scientific data about sperm whales.

> Sperm whales are able to last for up to two hours under water on a single breath.

One of the problems in studying sperm whales is that they rarely stay at the surface. They are the longest breath-holders of all mammals, able to last for up to two hours under water on a single breath. As a result they are able to dive to astonishing depths. They are the deepest diving of all earth's creatures and have been tracked 3000 metres below the surface. These leviathans are the largest of all the earth's carnivores, with males reaching a vast 16 metres in length. They inspired the legend of Moby Dick and terrified sailors for centuries. However, despite their considerable size, finding them in the endless miles of open sea is no easy task.

But, while it may be difficult to *see* sperm whales, it is a lot easier to hear them. Whales use a complex language of clicks to locate one another, communicate and mate. Different click patterns are used for each of these different purposes. A pattern of regularly spaced clicks, called 'usual' clicks, are used to locate their prey in the vast depths of the ocean. Shorter bursts, known as 'creaks', seem to be contact communication used to signal the whales' presence to other whales across vast distances. Slow, deep clicks seem to be a predominantly male 'language', probably used for mating. These are immensely loud, exceeding 230 decibels and equivalent to a rifle shot fired 1 metre from the ear. Recently, researchers have begun to understand how the whales are able to make such powerful sounds that they can be heard

ABOVE *The group of
socializing sperm whales
which included males,
suggested that this area
is an important breeding
ground.*

over 34 miles away, through the water. On top of their skull, sperm whales have a unique organ, called the spermaceti organ. It's filled with a milky white, semi-liquid wax which early whalers mistook for sperm – hence the whale's name. But it is actually a powerful sonar organ, whose highly variable muscle sheath allows the whale to create powerful, and variable, sound waves that resonate in the vast head of the whale before being projected.

Using underwater directional hydrophones it is possible to identify the location of the whales, and start to track their movement. Once close, the whale song is easily distinguishable under water by divers, a symphony of overlapping clicks. To the untrained ear this chaotic sound seems like mindless babble, but scientists have identified something fascinating in this complex whale language. As well as the patterns of clicks, sperm whales use codas, repeated rhythms, when they are communicating with one another. These codas are highly individual and seem to be much richer in meaning than the functional clicks. By comparing the codas of different clans of whales, the researchers have discovered that each clan has its own coda 'dialect'.

Diving with the sperm whales at San Pedro Martir was one of the highlights of the entire Oceans *expedition.*

In the same way that English-speakers have different regional accents, different whale families have individual, distinct coda dialects. Whales are strong clan animals and family members are known to stay in contact over decades. This unique dialect may be the way that members of the clan recognize each other when they are travelling across the world's oceans.

Using the hydrophone, the *Oceans* team tracked down a number of whales. However, every time they approached to make observations, the whales dived, flicking a languid 'cheerio' with their flukes as they plunged. Attempt after attempt ended in disappointment. Finally, at the end of an exhausting day, the whales came to the surface and stayed there.

Female sperm whales are highly social animals. They form large groups, or pods, of about 12 whales made up of females and their young. This structure allows the females to forage on deep dives for food, leaving the young at the surface, protected by the other females of the pod.

When young males reach six years of age, they begin to leave the pod, forming all-male 'bachelor' groups before gradually moving to a solitary existence. The females spend their lives in the group and stay together for decades, foraging, taking care of the young and socializing together.

Here in the Sea of Cortez, the group of whales at the surface begins to demonstrate this complex socializing behaviour. Five females start to roll over and around each other, gently rubbing and nuzzling each other. The movement resembles a hypnotic, almost balletic, dance as these vast leviathans continue to twist and turn, rolling over and over each other. The nuzzling seems to be a form of massage, which removes old skin, as well as a form of bonding between the members of the group. Females are known to socialize like this but to witness it at such close quarters is exceptionally rare. Under water it is a breathtaking spectacle as the five enormous sperm whales turn in a gentle, undulating knot. For the divers it is an extraordinary and very memorable experience.

Gradually, it becomes apparent that something else is going on – something that Dr Diane Gendron from the Centre of Interdisciplinary Marine Sciences in La Paz, who has accompanied the team, has never seen before. The group is not all female, as first thought, but includes some young males. As the group nuzzles and rubs together it is clear, not just that two of them are males, but that they are becoming sexually aroused. The erect penis on both is clearly visible. In addition, a large male is with the group, and he is also sexually aroused. This is a rare sight indeed, as males usually spend most of their time in colder waters.

It suggests that this area is an important breeding ground, and that we have witnessed important sexual activity. The encounter is not just an exhilarating experience but has ended in an extraordinary sighting, one that gives a unique insight into these formidable creatures.

As the expedition ends, this trip has revealed the complex interactions of a sea in flux. Man's overfishing has changed (and is still changing) the ecology of the Sea of Cortez in ways that are not always predictable. The adaptive behaviour of the sea lion, the massive explosion in the squid population and the rise in the number of sperm whales are all part of this shifting, changing ecology. This uniquely rich and fertile sea, thronging with abundant and spectacular marine life, is a remarkable window into a changing ocean world.

OPPOSITE *Stills from video footage of this extraordinary encounter clearly show that one of the male whales is sexually aroused.*

The encounter … has ended in an extraordinary sighting, one that gives a unique insight into these formidable creatures.

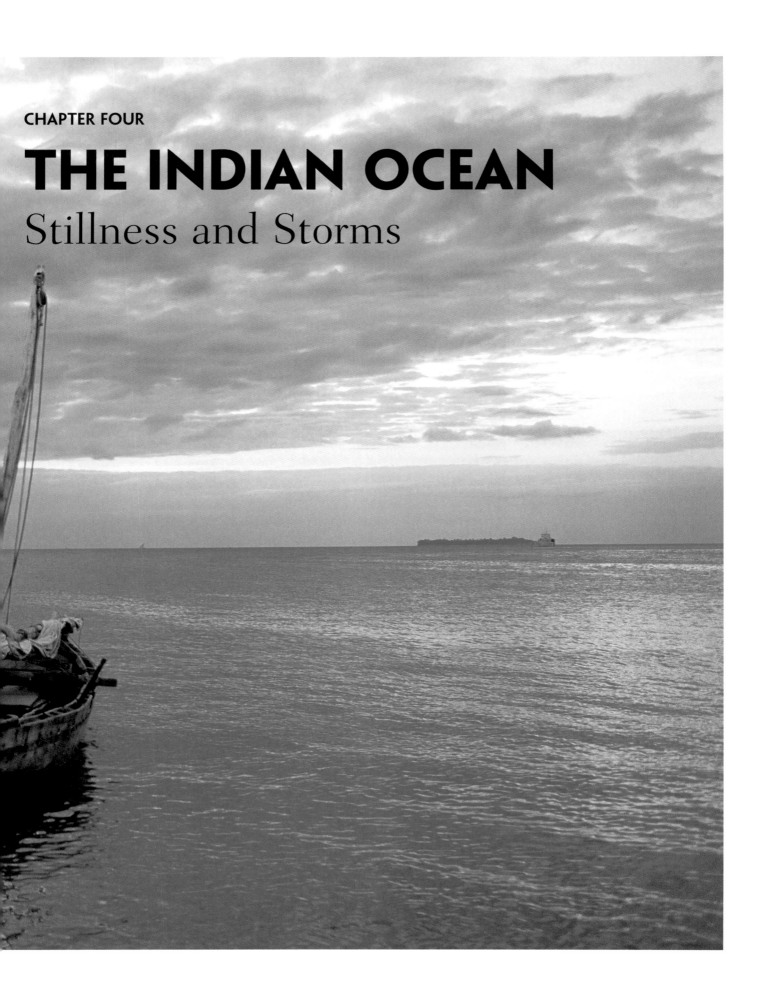

CHAPTER FOUR

THE INDIAN OCEAN

Stillness and Storms

PREVIOUS PAGE *Sunset at Stone Town, Zanzibar, and fishermen are out in force. It was the sea that first attracted settlers to this area.*

RIGHT *This* NASA *satellite image shows South India, the northern end of Sri Lanka and the Bay of Bengal, an area that produces severe cyclones.*

OPPOSITE *This computer generated image shows a topographical view of the Indian Ocean, it is the temperature differences between the sea and the surrounding land masses that cause the cataclysmic weather systems that characterize this contrasting ocean.*

ITS NAME ALONE CONJURES UP A PICTURE of exotic, bath-warm waters turned turquoise in the shallows by day-long sunshine. Indeed, this is a seductive jewel of an ocean nestling between Asia, the Middle East and Africa with sapphire depths that harbour rare and enigmatic creatures, dramatic sea monuments and vibrant, vivid reefs. But that is only one side of the story.

Ebbing and flowing over 25 million square miles, the Indian Ocean is the third largest on the planet. It is fringed by some spectacular beaches – think Seychelles, Goa, Maldives – and vast swathes of the world's population. And it was these densely populated areas that were devastated by the Boxing Day tsunami of 2004 which claimed the lives of an estimated 275,000 people and left countless thousands of others homeless, jobless and destitute. The catastrophe was caused by an undersea earthquake off the Sumatran coast, measuring a colossal 9.1 on the Richter scale and lasting for as long as ten minutes, dispatching waves from ocean to shore at speeds of 500 m.p.h. and at the height of city office blocks.

The Indian Ocean is not only subject to earthquakes but is also scythed through by one of the most powerful currents on earth, the Agulhas current. This and others like it have carved lands, destroyed ships and driven calamitous storms across the planet. To sum up, this seascape is by turns a place of sunshine and cyclonic rain, of stillness and storm, of extraordinary beauty and bone-chilling terror. The *Oceans* expedition has come here to explore the extreme contrasts of this powerful ocean, and to unravel its rich and complex legacy.

... a place ... of extraordinary beauty and bone-chilling terror.

When the team arrived at the port of Dar es Salaam, Tanzania, it was thronging with people. Shrieks of seabirds pierced the throbbing heartbeat of loud African music. Market traders shouted their wares, nearly drowned out by the groaning of dock machinery. The rich aromas of coconut oils, pungent spices and cooked fish hung like a cloud in the sea air. Along the harbour, at the end of a long walkway, stood *Kairos*, a sturdy and workmanlike boat that would be the team's cramped home as they explored the farthest reaches of the Indian Ocean. From the perspective of the boat's small cabin, the task ahead seemed immense.

We were to bob around an ocean that has fashioned islands and coastal lands, which supports 30 million people on its shores, is oil-rich, is crisscrossed by trade routes linking east and west and has currents that drive climate and weather patterns all over the world. More than any other ocean, this sea has shaped humanity's history and, furthermore, is driving our future.

FORCE OF THE CURRENTS

At the top of our list is an investigation into the massive force of the Indian Ocean currents which, perhaps more than anything, define its role. It's only recently that scientists have begun to understand just how important these currents are and knowledge is still limited. One of the problems is the difficulty of monitoring a complex three-dimensional environment deep below the surface of the sea and thousands of miles from land. But the *Oceans* team is about to play a part in changing that. We had been asked to take part in an international project designed to build a detailed 'real time' picture of the oceans in action. On the deck of *Kairos* is a long wooden box and inside is a state-of-the-art, robotic ocean-monitoring buoy, the latest addition to a network of 3000 similar buoys dotted throughout the oceans of the world. The cylindrical buoy, called an Argo float after the classical hero Jason's ship, is designed to dive to a depth of between 1000 and 2000 metres, drift at that level with the current and record temperature, salinity, depth and position. After ten days it propels itself to the surface and transmits the information by satellite to a receiving station before descending to complete its next ten-day cycle. Profiling floats like this have been in action since 2000. Within a few hours of launch, this rather insignificant looking buoy will begin sending data to scientists 5000 miles away in Liverpool, England, giving them a detailed picture of the currents and conditions in this part of the Indian Ocean.

If it's successfully launched, that is. Once the float is activated the team has precisely six hours to reach the remote deep-water location where it is to be sunk. There, the 2-metre-long float weighing 55 pounds needs to be dropped by deck crane to a diver waiting to guide it into position, 10 metres below the surface, ready for its first descent. It's a challenging manoeuvre. In deep, featureless waters divers can become disorientated and dive down instead of up towards the surface, with disastrous consequences.

It's a huge relief when the team watch the Argo float successfully disappear out of sight into the depths of the Indian Ocean on its first descent, to begin a recording career likely to last for at least four years and 150 cycles. The data the float sends back is not just of academic interest. The oceans and the atmosphere are inextricably linked. Throughout the world, the Argo armada of 3000 floats can measure the impact of global climate change and predict extreme weather, like the devastating 1998 El Niño, typhoons or hurricanes. In the Indian Ocean, the data can predict droughts and details of the wet seasons including how heavy the rains will be, and where and when they will fall.

OPPOSITE *Paul Rose waits to guide the Argo float into position. A deck crane on the* Kairos *drops the float so that he can guide it as it dives to begin a four-year cycle of recording.*

… the Argo armada of three thousand floats can measure the impact of global climate change …

CATACLYSMIC WEATHER SYSTEMS

Powerful monsoons that sweep across the tropics are caused by the difference in temperature between the sea and neighbouring land masses. A newly identified see-saw system, the Indian Ocean dipole, can cause cataclysmic weather. This complex, oscillating system was only identified in 1999 but its effects have been traced back through the coral record for over 10,000 years. In the positive phase of the dipole, sea surface temperatures in the west of the ocean are higher than in the east. This increases convection currents in the west and drags rain across to the lands there, causing severe rain and flooding in East Africa and the Middle East. At the same time, Indonesia, on the eastern side of the ocean, is starved of rain, causing droughts and forest fires. In its negative phase the dipole system reverses, bringing drought to Africa and torrential rains to Indonesia.

Just one day after the successful launch of the Argo float the team experiences the full might of the Indian Ocean weather systems. A tropical storm breaks. Strong winds whip the sea into a spume-topped frenzy. Then the rain comes down in torrents, the downpour sluicing the deck of the *Kairos* leaving water pouring relentlessly from the canvas sun cover. The rain has a curiously calming effect on the sea, flattening the cresting waves into gentle, stippled undulations. The team is en route to the island of Pemba, 50 miles off the African coast. Pemba is one of three islands off Tanzania, along with Zanzibar and Mafia Island, collectively known as the Zanzibar archipelago or the Spice Islands. Navigating the treacherous currents of the Indian Ocean is tricky at the best of times. In 45-knot winds, it's nearly impossible. But it's a graphic reminder of the power of this sea and its currents around these isles.

Pemba is the oldest of the islands, formed around 10 million years ago. It rose from the depths of the sea as a result of seismic activity and is now a mini subcontinent in its own right, sitting on the edge of the African continental plate. Above sea level it lives up to its Arabic name, 'the green island', as home to around three million clove trees. Around its perimeter the submerged landscape plunges into an 800-metre abyss, leaving sheer walls totally exposed to the force of the ocean. It's here that the best ocean architecture can be seen. These spectacular cliffs are decorated with crevices and overhangs sculpted by the southern equatorial current as it barrels across the Indian Ocean and swirls around the Zanzibar archipelago.

ABOVE *This satellite image shows the cyclonic storm Sidr, which hit the Bay of Bengal in 2007, producing winds of over 80 m.p.h.*

OPPOSITE *Soft coral grows in abundance on the sheer underwater cliffs of the vertical reef at Pemba.*

UNDERWATER SEA CLIFFS

The next mission for the *Oceans* team is to investigate one of the most dramatic features of this unique underwater seascape – a massive fissure carved deep into the face of the rock.

The sea is flat and featureless on the surface, and it's hard to envisage the sheer variety and drama of the seascape below water. Across the planet, our oceans hide mountain ranges higher than the Himalayas, trenches and ravines to rival the Grand Canyon, active undersea volcanoes that spit glowing lava, and even vast natural falls where sand, not water, plunges over ridges to fall 2000 metres into the deep.

The underwater sea cliffs at Pemba are at least as stunning as any found on land. Diving down the wall, the divers are struck by two things – the strength of the current and the abundantly busy sea life. A mass of colourful sea anemones crowds the rocky outcrops and moray eels, scorpionfish and hinged shrimp hide under the overhangs. Spectacular fish can be seen: razorfish; leaf fish, named for their shape and for an uncanny ability to remain motionless in the current; snowflake soap fish; brightly coloured titan triggerfish; and even the huge hump-headed wrasse, which can reach 2 metres in length and has the fascinating ability to change gender from female to male in adulthood. Rarer species such as dwarf lionfish and flying gurnards can also be found here.

As a tropical sea, the Indian Ocean is not known for its prolific aquatic life. But, just here, the ocean currents bring cold, nutrient-rich water up from the depths and create an oasis-like attraction for passing fish.

Buffeted by the current, the divers are pulled along the wall until they spot the opening – a gaping crack extending several metres into the rock. This vast fissure has been carved by the sea, the power of the current eroding the limestone rock to form the crevasse. The fissure is impressive but inside there is something more stunning: a breathtaking display of coral. Partly protected by the walls of the channel, the fissure has become a vertical reef, a bright hanging garden of soft corals, brain coral, dark green tree coral, forests of whip coral, barrel sponges and huge flat tablets of plate coral, growing outwards from the fissure walls. Vertical reefs are rare and to see one deep inside the base of an island is exceptional.

In Swahili the word for 'rock' and 'coral' is one and the same. In reality this couldn't be further from the truth. While rock is inert, coral is very much alive. Indeed, most corals are not just one species but two: part flora, part fauna – a fully functioning albeit diminutive ecosystem in their own right.

… mountain ranges higher than the Himalayas, trenches and ravines to rival the Grand Canyon …

OPPOSITE *Though the Indian Ocean is not known for the abundance of its sea life, the underwater cliffs at Pemba are an exception to the rule. Here, the currents bring cold, nutrient-rich water up from the depths and create an oasis for passing tropical fish.*

OVERLEAF *A spectacular view of sea life on the reef off the Glorioso Islands, near Madagascar, which shows a range of tropical fish including sweetlips, fairy bassiet and fusilier fish.*

was a time when the rulers and merchants built mosques and palaces, minted coinage and imported pottery and other goods from most of the known world – including China. At the time Europe was only just emerging from its cultural backwater at the start of the Middle Ages.

Ras Kisimani was inhabited by a mix of Africans, Arabs and traders from elsewhere in the Indian Ocean, principally the Persian Gulf regions. All were drawn to the riches that Africa had to offer: ivory, gold and spices – especially cloves, which were more valuable, pound for pound, than gold. These riches drew in Europeans in the wake of the Arab and Persian settlers.

By the end of the fifteenth century, the Portuguese explorer Vasco da Gama (1460–1524) arrived at the Spice Islands. He was surprised to find a developed society with thriving trade, a monetary economy, wealthy merchants and sheiks. Within a few years, the Portuguese fleet returned and took control of the region, a rule that lasted two centuries. At the heart of this protectorate was the slave trade, controlled for centuries by Portugal and condoned by every other major power and ethnic group.

... spices – especially cloves, which were more valuable, pound for pound, than gold.

In the nineteenth century, even after slavery was made illegal (in 1807 in Britain) between 10,000 and 30,000 African people per year were shipped as slaves from the Spice Islands. At Ras Kisimani the trade continued until the immense force of nature put a stop to it. The cataclysmic cyclone that tore off the headland and destroyed the town arrived just a year before slavery was finally outlawed in the region. Now all that remains of the rich history of Ras Kisimani are a few sunken remains, protected and preserved by the sea.

The story of the storm is preserved here in the heart of the coral. Coral grows at a rate of about 1–3 centimetres a year, adding to its calcareous outer skeleton. This forms annual growth rings in the coral, rather like tree rings. And, like trees, coral can survive for hundreds of years, forming a living record across centuries. By taking a core from the coral and analysing the growth in each year, scientists can both identify extreme weather events of the past and predict future events. Part of this analysis is done by viewing the thin 5-centimetre-diameter cores under ultraviolet light. In this light clear, fluorescing bands are visible, showing yearly growth. In a year with high rainfall or soaring temperatures, skeletal calcification of the coral is low and therefore growth is limited. These cores ultimately record massive weather events in the Indian Ocean, like the the cyclone that swept Ras Kisimani into the sea, the devastating 1998 El Niño and the impact of the newly discovered Indian Ocean dipole.

… coral can survive for hundreds of years … a living record across the centuries.

DANGEROUS WATERS

The Agulhas current is the second fastest in the world, and its complex and unpredictable flow patterns make it the most dangerous to navigate. For centuries, this current prevented European explorers rounding the cape at the tip of Africa. When Portuguese explorer Bartholomew Dias (c.1455–1500) became the first to do so in 1486 he called it the 'Cape of Storms'. Later, Portugal's King John renamed it the Cape of Good Hope to reflect the optimism of travellers who had rounded it and were heading to the rich trading areas beyond. Even now it is dangerous and difficult to navigate. It's why the waters further south are some of the most unexplored in the world.

And that is the next destination of the expedition. we are leaving the exotic Spice Islands and heading south, to the remote waters off the coast of Mozambique where the team aims to investigate the world's largest colony of manta rays, giants of the deep with wingspans of up to 8 metres.

The largest population of manta rays ever recorded numbered over 600, just offshore in Mozambique's southern waters. These enigmatic gliders are the largest of all rays. But, unlike their close cartilaginous cousins the sharks, mantas are not predatory. Bar the odd small fish and krill they feed almost exclusively on plankton.

Mantas often feed at the surface on small zooplankton by funnelling them into their mouths with specialized head fins – called cephalic fins – that unfurl into scoops. When these fins are rolled back up into a non-feeding position they look like devilish horns.

Fishermen and early divers called manta rays 'devilfish' and who could blame them? They move fast and have accidentally swum into ships' ropes, anchor lines or even into hard-hat divers' air hoses. Rays can't swim backwards so, when they get tangled, they just try to power forwards, thrash around and often leap clear of the water. There are old stories of mantas drowning divers, and towing fishing boats out to sea before crushing them.

Mantas must eat a huge amount of plankton to survive and tend to congregate in fast-flowing, nutrient-rich waters. The Indian Ocean currents off the Mozambique coast curl around a headland and concentrate the plankton into a relatively tight area, making it an ideal feeding ground. But that's not the only attraction. Below the surface, an ocean reef has formed into a unique ecosystem centred on the rays – a cleaning station.

All fish carry unwanted hitchhikers, usually parasites. Mantas depend on the reef's 'valet' service available at cleaning stations. Here, different 'cleaner' fish feast on parasites and dead tissue off the larger fishes' skin. This artful symbiotic relationship provides food and protection for the 'cleaners' and considerable health benefits for those being serviced. There is one overwhelming criterion for a manta cleaning station – a strong current to enable the manta to remain stationary while still passing fresh oxygenated water through its gills. The sites are mostly found at the top of reef walls.

ABOVE *The waters to the south of Mozambique are home to the largest population of manta rays in the world. These huge fish feed almost exclusively on plankton. They congregate where the ocean currents ensure that the plankton is concentrated in a relatively small area.*

The plan was to take a low-flying plane and scan the area from the air, while a boat waited in the vicinity ready to head towards any sightings. The search would be made more difficult by the fact that dugongs are notoriously shy, easily stressed and quick to dive at the sound of an engine.

Dugongs do not swim fast over long distances, and tire easily if chased. It is thought that their metabolism stays in low gear so that seagrass alone can sustain them. On top of that, their flesh reportedly tastes delicious, making them attractive prey for whales, sharks and crocodiles. Humans once hunted them for meat, hides and oil, but today, most populations are protected by law. Hunting, though, is only one cause of their decline. The destruction of seagrass habitats has been a significant factor, as has entanglement of these slow-moving animals in fishing nets. Nor do dugongs do much to help themselves, having an extraordinary low reproductive rate. Females do not reach sexual maturity until ten years of age, and even then only give birth to a single calf, every three to seven years. Females therefore tend to produce only one calf in a lifetime – and do not give birth at all if food is scarce. As a result, even the slightest reduction in the survival of adults has a devastating impact on the sustainability of the population. Dugongs are on the International Union for Conservation of Nature (IUCN) vulnerable list and the Bazaruto archipelago is believed to be the next place where they will become extinct unless urgent action is taken.

The team's search for dugongs is hampered by the weather, which is now almost routinely poor. Storms blowing in make it impossible to launch the plane, and even when there is a break the sediment stirred up in the sea makes it impossible to see anything under water. Also, shortages of fuel mean there is only time for a few short air reconnaissance trips. But on one of these two dark smudges are spotted in the water below. Dugongs! And, even more excitingly, a mother and a calf. The boat follows the direction they are travelling in, aiming to steer round them in a wide sweep and drift without motors into a position that allows a closer sighting.

Finally, there they are. Not just the mother and her calf, but a group of five, swimming gracefully through the water. From observation the animals appear healthy, and the sighting of the calf indicates that food is plentiful. It is a special moment for the team, seeing these rare creatures in their natural habitat for perhaps the last time. But the health of this group gives a ray of hope that there is still time to protect the population here, to allow this legendary creature, this secret siren, to survive.

At the end of the day a glorious sunset transforms the ocean. Recent storms are forgotten in the golden stillness, with the sea calm and serene in the sky's fiery glow.

> Females … tend to produce only one calf in a lifetime.

Riches on the Seabed

Perhaps the real relationship between mankind and the sea is wrought in the wrecks that litter the floor of this ocean. Currents, not mermaid song, inspire its deadly power. Many ships have been swept along the currents or caught in the changing winds, to founder on the reefs or rocks below the surface. The sea has taken many thousands of lives and many more thousands of tonnes of cargo over the years, but now people are taking some of it back. Modern-day salvagers plunder the riches of sunken treasure.

ABOVE *Paul Rose dives down to the wreck of the* Paraportiani, *a victim of the powerful East African coastal current in 1967.*

These days the bounty is more likely to be the bronze of a propeller rather than gold or silver doubloons, but the plunder is still controversial. To archaeologists, wrecks are valuable sites, preserving a moment in time, an archaeological resource that exists nowhere else and can reveal untold riches in terms of understanding our past. For local salvage operators, it's a way of exploiting the sea, no different from the exploitation that has always been used to provide a livelihood.

The *Paraportiani* was carrying a full cargo of wheat from Romania to Jeddah on what should have been a routine 1800-mile passage. But in 1967 the Suez Canal was closed during the Arab-Israeli war and that meant her only option was a 12,400-mile passage out of the Black Sea and across the Mediterranean into the Atlantic, to pass down the west coast of Africa, around the Cape of Good Hope, up into the Indian Ocean and finally north into the Red Sea.

I can imagine the wheelhouse on the night of 25 October 1967 as the captain of the *Paraportiani* and his officers worked out their position. The long voyage had taken its toll on the 40-year-old ship and among the broken equipment was the radar. Without its magic eye, the captain only had a sextant and compass. And because of overcast skies he had not had a good sun sight for an accurate sextant fix for days. He could not even take the safer route of going way out to the east into more open waters as the ship was by now desperately short of supplies and water. So he was committed to taking her in to Mombasa to resupply.

The wheelhouse would have been as dark as possible with all white lights extinguished, the compass, depth finder and charts lit by dim red lights in an effort to preserve delicate night vision. A crewman lighting up a cigarette in sight of the wheelhouse would have been severely chastised. It would take fully 20 minutes to restore the night vision damaged by the flash of his match.

Unknown to the men of the *Paraportiani* they were being forced towards land in the grip of the powerful East African coastal current, reaching speeds of 5 knots. Features on the sea bottom did not offer any clues that they were approaching land as there is no gentle slope leading to shallow waters. Instead, Pemba Island sits at the top of the continental shelf with water depths going from deep ocean to shallow reef in an instant.

The combination of bad weather, their uncertain position and the force of the current could only equal disaster. And so it was that the ship ran up hard on to the Panza Reef at the southern tip of Pemba Island.

Her radioed distress call was answered by the Mombasa signal station and relayed to the Kenyan navy at Mtongwe who deployed two patrol boats to attempt a rescue. In the meantime 19 of the crew had taken to the lifeboats and rowed ashore where they were arrested by the Green Guard, a local Pemba militia unit. During the arrest one of the crew was shot for refusing to hand over a case of Scotch whisky he had rescued from the ship. At the same time the Kenyan navy sent a boat to the *Paraportiani* to bring the remaining crew ashore – they, too, were arrested. The confusion was all made good later when the crew were taken to Mombasa, the shot crewman was treated and the whole crew was repatriated to Greece.

Unlike the *Paraportiani* our dive boat was fully equipped with the best navigation equipment, including up-to-date paper charts, electronic charts, detailed current information and an array of back-up electronics. We also had powerful engines and perfect weather. But even so, it was too dangerous for us to anchor at Panza Reef, so we stood off in safer, deep water and ran our dive boats over to the wreck.

The great East African coastal current was ripping across the *Paraportiani* so we had to drift-dive her. That is, enter the water upcurrent from her position and let the current drift us along the wreck. We dropped on to the reef and flew towards the stern. She is a beautiful wreck. Mostly intact, the collapsed hull and twisted steel are a testament to the power of the Indian Ocean's currents. As we whizzed around her we ducked behind companionway doors, the boilers and any good-sized object to stop ourselves drifting off, and when we did stop the current was so strong that I could feel my mask vibrating. Our exhaust bubbles went sideways instead of straight up to the surface.

We let go of the ship's rail and, accompanied by hundreds of fish, continued our underwater high-speed flight down the port side and over the mast, which was lying across the hull with the top pointing out to the deep shelf. We scuttled behind the rudder to rest by the propeller, its massive four blades giving us a calm eddy in the current. We saw the locals had been salvaging bits of the wreck. They had taken some relatively easily available valuable pieces, such as brass portholes, and had been trying to cut through the massive propeller shaft. If they were successful the propeller would sell for a small fortune.

As we surfaced my last sight of the wreck was the huge shaft, partly buried deep in the seabed, half cut through, and a large collection of lifting tackle left in place by the local salvors. I thought it was great that the Pemba Island villagers were salvaging some of the ship. It looked like a relatively sustainable and environmentally friendly livelihood. The island is not wealthy and the sale of those wreck pieces could keep a community going for years. My co-diver Lucy, on the other hand, was deeply concerned that the salvors were destroying the site. She felt their salvage activities were part of a problem that encourages looting of vessels of all ages and great historical value.

We left the wreck to its uncertain future – archaeological site or source of income?

…the current was so strong that I could feel my mask vibrating.

PLIGHT OF THE SEA HORSE

As a consequence of warm waters that are less rich than others in nutrients, the Indian Ocean is not hugely productive, so it is not fertile territory for the commercial fishing industry. However, two species are exploited – sea horses and sharks. Populations of both are in sharp decline as a result of massive industrial operations to supply the highly lucrative Chinese market.

Sea horses, in particular, are prized as key ingredients in traditional medicine, to treat asthma, heart disease, skin disorders and impotence. In the East they are believed to be a powerful aphrodisiac and around 20 million animals a year are killed and sold for use in traditional medicines in China, Indonesia, the Philippines and other places. It's a massive trade with good-quality sea horses selling for about $550 per pound and even puny specimens sell for hundreds of dollars a pound. Accordingly, nine out of 33 sea-horse species are on the IUCN 'red list' as vulnerable, and one species in the Indian Ocean is officially endangered.

Sea horses are fascinating and uncommon creatures who shelter in algae, corals, mangrove swamps and seagrass beds, deeply disguised and almost hidden to the human eye. They can change colour to match their background and grow long skin appendages to mimic algae. They let encrusting organisms settle on them and can remain virtually motionless for hours at a time. They are delicate, slow-moving animals, which is why they rely so heavily on camouflage to catch their prey.

Famously, the male becomes 'pregnant' and carries the eggs that the female deposits in his pouch, caring for them for two to three weeks until he gives birth. The male and female mating pair is monogamous and most sea horses stay with each other for life. It is due to their monogamy and their attachment to a single, very specific habitat that sea horses are especially vulnerable. If a sea horse is moved or loses its mate it is highly unlikely to find another mate and continue to reproduce. So the intensive fishing of these creatures has the potential to quickly decimate the sea-horse population.

OPPOSITE *A seahorse can change colour to match its background. They rely on this camouflage to catch their food.*

In the East they are believed to be a powerful aphrodisiac and around 20 million animals a year are killed …

THE CORAL NURSERY

The long expedition is coming to an end. Over the past four weeks, the team has explored the impact of the sea on mankind and seen the effect of human activity on the sea. And now, as the final stages of the trip loom, we are able

OPPOSITE *All the world's coral reefs are under threat, but an experiment being carried out on the reef in Zanzibar is bringing a ray of hope to the situation. 'Cuttings' from soft coral are being grown in nurseries on an undisturbed part of the reef before being transplanted into a degraded section. In this way it is hoped to regenerate the entire area. Early results are encouraging.*

to reflect on one particular example that epitomizes the intense relationship between us and this complex and contradictory sea: the coral nursery.

At the beginning of the trip we saw how the power of the Indian Ocean carved its islands and created the conditions to make a stunning coral reef. But the impact of human-induced global warming has meant that in other parts of the ocean the sea temperature is rising and killing off the vital algae that live within the coral. As the algae die, the coral returns to its natural colour – white. Often the coral is recolonized with algae, but in many parts of the Indian Ocean the coral never recovers and the reefs are blighted with bleached, dead coral. But now there's a new and ingenious solution being pioneered on the reefs off the coast of Zanzibar. Diving these reefs, it is clear they are not as healthy as those at Pemba Island. Part of the problem is global warming and the devastating 1998 El Niño, but another factor is the expansion of the tourist industry in Zanzibar. The coral has been a key tourist attraction, but along with the tourist divers has come pollution, sediment that chokes the coral, and physical damage both accidental and deliberate. The local people rely on the income from tourism, so there is reluctance to stop the tourist divers coming; but there is also determination to try and restore the reefs.

Scientists working in Zanzibar take the expedition team away from the main coral reef to an undisturbed part of the ocean where a remarkable sight meets our eyes. A coral garden is growing on stretched nets suspended at midwater level. There are several nets strung flat and swaying gently in the current, and on each one is a mini forest of tiny coral 'cuttings' nestled into 9-centimetre rubber tubes secured to the nets. The scientists here are regenerating the reefs by using principles of land-based horticulture. The technique has been used successfully on land to regenerate forests; now it is being applied under water to coral. Tiny cuttings, called nubbins or spats, are carefully taken from healthy 'mother' coral and cultivated in this more protected environment for 292 days until they have grown into healthy, midsized sections of coral. This coral is then transplanted into a bleached or degraded area of reef where it's hoped it will establish, and regenerate the entire area. This is still an experimental technique, but early results suggest it is highly effective. The free-floating, midwater nurseries are safe from predators and sedimentation, and the water flow around the nets brings a constant supply of plankton, and oxygen dissolved in the water.

All around the world coral reefs are in crisis. According to the UN a third of these vital ecosystems have been lost already, and by 2030 the figure is predicted to be nearer 60 per cent. The hope is that coral

All around the world coral reefs are in crisis ... a third of these vital ecosystems have been lost already...

gardening may be the key to preventing this. This simple technique, being used for the first time in the Indian Ocean, could help restore coral reefs all over the world.

It is a fitting end to the Indian Ocean story: a perfect example of the complex interdependence between mankind and this powerful ocean. This trip has revealed an ocean of extremes. A sea that contains both mythical, enigmatic creatures and some of the world's largest fish; a sea with tides and currents that can both build lands and destroy them; and, above all, a sea that is intimately linked to the lives, history and future of the 30 million people who depend on it.

by continental plates moving apart. It is the world's youngest ocean, only starting to open a mere 38 million years ago. And it's still growing, widening at just over a centimetre a year, about the rate of a fingernail's growth. But, perhaps most remarkably, on its fringes is the site of a completely new ocean. Fast-forward 200 million years and there could be water where the Horn of Africa presently sits.

We've travelled to the very south of the Red Sea in Djibouti, a remote country in the Horn of Africa bordering Ethiopia, Eritrea and Somalia. Our destination is the Devil's Cauldron, a bay on the edge of the Red Sea and one of only two places in the world where you can dive to see the birth of an ocean (the other being in the chillier climes of Iceland).

Lying at the bottom of the bay is the westernmost section of a huge crack, or rift, which divides the unstable African and Arabian plates. These plates are pulling apart, creating the new ocean.

Normally, these tectonic processes are hidden under glaciers or at the bottom of an ocean floor and covered by thousands of metres of sea water. But in Djibouti the evidence that the earth is being ripped apart can be seen in the shallow waters of this bay. Moreover, it is happening rapidly. During a three-week spell of tectonic shifting in 2005 the rift grew by 8 metres. Its rampant activity was observed from the European Space Agency satellite.

> … it is the world's youngest ocean … And it's still growing.

AN OCEAN BEGINS

The team heads into the middle of the bay, passing Devil's Island, an extinct volcano rearing up from the water. Tremors are frequently felt in the surrounding area – our local guide felt one just a few days previously – and the surrounding land is strewn with lava flows. The water is jet black in colour from the volcanic basalt rock that lines the bay's floor.

As the divers descend the water column one thing is immediately striking. There is abundant life under the surface of the water compared with the barren volcanic desert on the land above, drawn here for both the relative safety it provides from predators and for the swirling wealth of nutrients.

At around 30 metres the divers catch their first glimpse of the crack, or La Faille as it is called locally, cutting deep into the rock to the earth's crust below. Strange bridges of basalt have formed across it, like walkways for the millions of marine creatures living here. The rift is narrow, deep and dark. The divers descend, dropping into the rift and sinking between the two

> Tremors are frequently felt in the surrounding area …

OPPOSITE *The ragged and desolate coastline of the Devil's Cauldron on the Bay of Ghoubett in the south-eastern corner of the Red Sea – a site of ongoing tectonic activity.*

ABOVE *Devil's Island, an extinct volcano in the middle of the Devil's Cauldron.*

OPPOSITE *An Afar tribesman walks across one of the vast salt pans on Lake Assal. This nomadic Muslim tribe that lives on the shores of the Red Sea will give its name to the new ocean.*

tectonic plates. It is awe-inspiring to imagine the immense subterranean power that has pulled these vast plates apart.

As the plates move, fresh magma is forced up from the earth's core to fill the gap. As the gap widens, more magma rises up and solidifies to form a new ocean floor. This is how all the oceans on our planet have formed. Here in Djibouti, as the plates pull apart, the waters of the Red Sea and the Gulf of Aden will flood in, covering the land and creating a new ocean over this corner of Africa. At the moment its shoreline is impossible to predict. Some scientists think the Horn of Africa will break off from the mainland in the process. Even though the new ocean won't exist for maybe 200 million more years, it has already been given a name, the Afar Ocean, called after the immediate region and the nomadic tribe that inhabits it.

One place that will certainly be part of the new ocean is the extraordinary Lake Assal. A crater lake 6¼ miles long and 4⅓ miles wide, it registers as the lowest place in Africa at 154 metres below sea level. Although it is completely landlocked, there is a steady flow of sea water into it through hundreds of tiny cracks in the surrounding rock. Due to the constant supply of sea water, and high levels of evaporation, the lake is the saltiest body of water in the

world, some ten times saltier than the nearby Red Sea. This makes it an extremely hostile environment for animals. As a result, only colonies of bacteria are found here.

WHITE GOLD

The highly saline waters give rise to the vast salt pans that surround the lake and which are still mined today. Geologists believe that in the past the Red Sea became as salty as Lake Assal when it partially dried out as a result of fluctuating sea levels. It's this fluctuation that has made the sea one of the most important sites in human history and given the team an opportunity to glimpse its long-distant past. When sea levels dropped, this allowed our earliest ancestors to cross out of Africa and begin to spread across the world.

> When sea levels dropped, this allowed our earliest ancestors … to spread across the world.

The notion that the human race originated in Africa is not new; Darwin first mooted the idea in the mid-nineteenth century. Of course, then there were no fossils or artefacts to support his claim. However, recent findings in Africa of ancient remains of *Homo sapiens* and the tools and weapons our ancestors used, point towards an African origin of the human race. Scientists have used these skeletal remains combined with DNA patterning of present-day world populations to estimate an emergence of *Homo sapiens* in Africa around 150,000 to 195,000 years ago. We also know that these populations had dispersed from Africa to most other parts of the world at least 60,000 years ago, where they replaced pre-existing populations, such as the European Neanderthals.

LOOKING FOR CLUES

Some of the most central questions as to exactly how and why this dramatic population dispersal took place have never been clearly resolved. The team heads on to Eritrean soil to search for clues. As some early modern humans made their way north across the plains of Africa, the Red Sea would probably have been the first body of water they had ever encountered. The area was perfect, being safe, high and dry, and, remarkably, with abundant fresh water. The wells are still used by the military today. Shellfish could be easily collected – there was no dangerous hunting and no need for cooking – and only simple tools were needed to open them. Here, there are signs that early humans made a home by the sea.

Multicoloured Dive

Our passage east from Massawa was idyllic. Strong southerly winds heaped up the waves and hundreds of birds and dolphins accompanied our rolling journey. The hot dry wind combined with tonnes of spray coming on board from this, the warmest and saltiest sea in the world, meant we arrived at the reefs completely caked in salt. It was a great passage and, of course, it felt equally good to anchor in the shelter of the reef and hose ourselves off.

Fewer than a hundred divers come here in a year. By comparison, the northern part of the Red Sea hosts thousands of divers each year. So it follows that these reefs would be in a beautiful, pristine condition. But I had no idea just how remarkable they really are.

As I descended through the surging surface water and into relatively calmer depths at the reef edge it was obvious that these dives were going to be very special. The reef was exploding with colour and life. Soft corals, sponges, hard corals, fish of all sizes in their thousands and in every colour added to the wonderful burst of vibrancy in this immaculate unspoiled reef. So I felt a twinge of guilt that I was carrying a set of chisels and a large hammer. But my work here could help coral everywhere.

The coral reefs of Eritrea may have a secret weapon that just might be able to save threatened corals around the world. The hypothesis is that in this area the traditional algae partner is ditched for a more durable variety. So my job on this dive was to take samples of the coral and algae. There is every chance that the heat-tolerant algae could be transplanted to act as a 'booster vaccine' for other corals.

To help understand the reef I dived again at night. Reefs change their aspect at night, mostly due to the feeding and hunting habits of the marine life. And strangely, some corals have the remarkable ability to fluoresce.

My dives here had a special twist: this would be the very first time that work on coral fluorescence had ever been done on these reefs. Instead of my normal dive lights I carried blue lights to excite the fluorescing coral and I wore a special filter over the top of my dive mask to enable me to study the phenomenon. It was a shock to arrive at the reef – I had to keep peering underneath my mask filter to stay orientated as I felt as if I was back in a 1960s light show.

> … these dives were going to be very special. The reef was exploding with colour and life.

... I could have spent months diving here.

I was surrounded by fields of brilliant green-yellow and purple. Some of the hard corals glowed only on the tops, some glowed at their edges and random patches of shocking colours were everywhere. It was so beautiful that I struggled to concentrate on my observations and measurements. On shallow dives like this you can spend a long time under water, but not long enough for me – I could have spent months diving here.

These reefs may have a successful combination of fluorescing proteins in the coral tissue and heat-resistant algal partners. It seems obvious that this has allowed the coral to thrive in what would be a hazardous environment for all other corals. But despite all the ongoing research, nobody really knows how this works.

Some scientists think corals use fluorescent pigments to regulate light. As in plants, strong light can exacerbate the effects of other stresses and, consequently, these pigments can protect them from a variety of stresses. This has yet to be scientifically confirmed – but our studies indicate that these fluorescent corals cope better with temperature stress.

So do we transplant the heat-resistant algae to threatened corals, or let a natural evolutionary adaptation occur? And what part does the amazing fluorescence play in all this?

The only way to find out is to increase our ocean research. The level of interest in the health of the sea has never been higher and the dives made by the *Oceans* expedition on these stunning reefs in the Red Sea contribute to that research.

BELOW *Our team's camera captured the brilliant colours of the fluorescent coral in this unspoilt part of the Red Sea.*

OVERLEAF *The sun sets on the Red Sea and the coral reef prepares its night time light show.*

Conshelf II was a defining effort in the study of diving physiology and so is Aquarius, an underwater laboratory off the coast of Florida funded by the US National Oceanographic and Atmospheric Administration. By employing the principles of saturation diving, it enables scientists to spend days studying marine life while minimizing the risks of decompression sickness. NASA also used its facilities to train astronauts to work under conditions of high atmospheric pressure.

Most of the buildings of Conshelf II may have gone, but the marine life that drew Jacques Cousteau to this sea is still rich and abundant. Here in the southern Red Sea, with little fishing or tourism, we are in an unspoiled ecosystem and have a chance to locate species that are threatened or endangered elsewhere. It's a rare opportunity. Scientists know little of what animals are present in many areas of the Red Sea because of the difficulty of getting access to this part of the world.

… the marine life that drew Jacques Cousteau to this sea is still rich and abundant.

SHARK HUNT

For the expedition, the species that were the focus of most concern were sharks. All over the world shark numbers have been decimated due to the commercial demand for fins. And we already knew that one of the hardest hit was the scalloped hammerhead shark. This curious-looking shark with its head flattened to form a wide 'hammer' will be listed on the 2008 IUCN 'red list' as globally endangered. These sharks used to swim in huge numbers but now it is rare to find groups. Just to spot them at all is a wonderful privilege with every sighting adding important information about their fate.

All over the world shark numbers have been decimated due to the commercial demand for fins.

To find them, or any sharks, requires patience and a long spell under water, so the team decided to use re-breathers in place of normal scuba equipment to give themselves the maximum amount of time under water.

Hammerheads generally cruise at huge depths, more than 200 metres looking for food, but it seems that the highly sensitive electroreceptors on their hammer-shaped noses can also pick up minute changes in water temperature that would be indecipherable to humans. The theory is that hammerheads use haloclines, where hot and cold bodies of water meet, as a reference point for changing temperatures. The *Oceans* team planned to wait at these haloclines in the hope of spotting the sharks.

The team carried out a series of dives and during them were lucky enough to spot a number of rare species. A sailfish shadowed one of our divers. At a metre long, the sailfish is the fastest fish in the ocean with a huge dorsal fin which inspired its name. When the sail is lifted up in order to scare off predators, the sailfish is a majestic sight. A silky shark also swam by. Sporadically menacing, these sharks are solitary by nature and have been named for the sheen and smoothness of their skin. A number of reef sharks surrounded another diver. But, although the view of the divers was largely obscured by a multitude of fish, no hammerheads were in sight.

It was only in the last minutes of the final dive before the end of the expedition that they finally saw hammerheads. And what a sight they were. A huge school of around 30 was swimming rapidly in the distance. Hammerheads are highly efficient swimmers, using the hammer-shaped head as an

> ## At a metre long, the sailfish is the fastest fish in the ocean.

aerofoil. In cross-section the hammer is similar to the shape of an aeroplane wing, with a flattened lower surface and a rounded upper surface, making the shark more hydrodynamic. This shape may also produce lift, enabling them to pursue prey while following their every move. The divers relished the spectacle before the sharks peeled off into the deep.

To see such a large school is a remarkably positive sign. It means that in this area at least there are viable and healthy populations, when in other places all over the globe numbers are declining and the species is threatened. And, as we come to the end of our time here, we realize that this is what the Red Sea has given us: a sign of hope for the oceans of the world. Its coral shows that the vital rainforests of the sea can adapt to warmer waters, and the vibrancy of its ecosystems shows that the oceans can harbour abundant, diverse extraordinary life. Our oceans are fragile, but here at least there are signs that they can, and will, survive.

ABOVE *Though they had to wait, the team were finally rewarded with a display of superb swimming by a number of hammerhead sharks. Endangered in a number of the world's oceans, the school witnessed in the Red Sea is regarded as a sign of hope for the survival of this fascinating species.*

PUNCHING ABOVE ITS WEIGHT

The Southern Ocean covers nearly 8 million square miles and is the second smallest of all our oceans. Only its opposite number, the Arctic Ocean, is smaller. But what it lacks in size it makes up for in significance. This ocean carries the world's largest current, the Antarctic circumpolar current; 13,000 miles in length, transporting 130 million cubic metres of water per second – that's a hundred times the flow of all the world's rivers combined. This vast current moves nutrients and heat around the globe and has a powerful influence on the world's climate. While not large itself, the Southern Ocean links all three of our biggest oceans: the Pacific, the Atlantic and the Indian oceans, acting as a vital crossroads of the major water masses of the world. But perhaps most importantly, the Southern Ocean currently plays a critical role in moderating climate change.

… the Southern Ocean currently plays a critical role in moderating climate change.

OPPOSITE ABOVE *Forests of giant sea kelp form a unique system of varied micro environments for their inhabitants with a sunny and light canopy, a partially shaded mid-section and a dark sea floor, similar to forests on land.*

OPPOSITE BOTTOM *The red handfish is just one of the native Tasmanian species that survives in the kelp.*

The cold waters here provide rich nutrients for huge numbers of plankton and algae, which absorb carbon dioxide. The Southern Ocean is the biggest carbon sink in the world, absorbing as much as 8 per cent of the global carbon dioxide emissions from human activity. However, this sea also offers a stark warning. Parts of the ocean here are warming up over two and a half times faster than anywhere else on the planet, and the impact is far-reaching.

This is a sea of wild and rugged beauty, astonishing seascapes and extraordinary creatures. It's a remote and unfamiliar sea and, as the team waited for the weather to clear, there was a sense that this, of all the expeditions, would be the most challenging – but perhaps also the most rewarding. Astonishingly within an hour the sea was flat calm. The wind dropped and the air took on the pellucid clarity that is characteristic of the aftermath of the most intense storms. Moments later the expedition was under way as we set off to reach our first target.

RAINFORESTS OF THE SEA

The *Oceans* team is headed for Tasmania's south-eastern coast, north of the colourfully named Pirates Bay, to investigate one of this region's most iconic marine giants. Giant kelp is a brown seaweed. But it's no ordinary seaweed. This is the monster of all seaweeds. Kelp is the largest marine plant in the world, producing 'towers' of fronds that stretch 30 metres to the surface. The largest kelp plant ever recorded reached a staggering 65 metres – that's taller than Nelson's Column in London. They're also the fastest-growing marine plants, climbing 30–60 centimetres vertically every day. An entire forest can spring up in a week. Each plant has a holdfast

The largest kelp plant ever recorded reached a staggering 65 metres.

that attaches to the rocky sea floor, and a long, slender stalk, or stipe, from which grow long leaf-like blades called fronds. And on each frond are the gas-filled bladders, or pneumatocysts, that keep the giant plant buoyant and upright in the sea.

These majestic plants grow in vast 'forests' under water and, like forests on land, the dense canopy of fronds forms a system of micro environments, with a sunny canopy region, a partially shaded middle section and a darkened sea floor. Each 'level' of the kelp forest shelters different marine life. These are, in a way, the rainforests of the sea – one of the most biologically productive habitats in the marine environment.

The unique ecosystem provides a home for many elusive and enigmatic animals. The pot-belly sea horse and big-belly sea horse both live here as do larger fish like the golden weedfish and the crested weedfish. Some animals,

like the poisonous, spiky, cowfish are found nowhere else in the world. This is where the smallest octopus in the world lives, the pygmy octopus, which measures just 3 centimetres across. Rock lobster and abalone, and, perhaps most enigmatic of all, the tiny, red and yellow, spotted and fringed weedy sea dragon, depend on the kelp forests.

The expedition is here to investigate the current state of the kelp. The first survey is by helicopter. The team is armed with a map of what are traditionally the best kelp areas but from the air, the news is not good. There is no sign of lush mats of kelp or dense forests. In many places there is nothing at all and in others there are just sparse scattered clumps of kelp.

Giant kelp is a typical cold-water species and occurs in shallow coastal regions with cold, nutrient-rich waters. Sea currents are essential to allow fresh nutrients to be delivered across the kelp fronds, and a rocky sea floor is needed to provide a secure attachment for the holdfast. Tasmania's cold clean waters and rocky coastline therefore provide the perfect habitat.

Or at least they did. Over the last ten years the sea temperature here has risen by 1.5°C – faster than any other sea in the world – and now the *minimum* temperature of the water off the east coast of Tasmania is 11.5°C, with the average much higher. For kelp, which thrives in 6–14°C, these temperatures are not ideal. And as a result, over the last ten years there's been a dramatic decline. Just 40 years ago the waters all along the coast were thronged with lush kelp forests, stretching over 124 miles and easily visible from the air as the fronds reached up to cover large areas of the sea surface. Now the kelp has all but vanished from many regions.

The helicopter flies over Fortescue Bay on the east coast of the island, which used to be one of the richest areas of kelp forest. There were tales of kelp so dense that people could walk from one side of the extensive bay to another across seaweed mats. Now there are just a few straggly plants.

Under water the picture is even more depressing. The kelp plants, once so majestic, are spindly and instead of the lush canopy of fronds the divers find a straggly covering of leaf-like blades. The problem is easy to identify. Measurement of the sea temperature shows it is 14°C; at that temperature kelp struggles to survive. But on the sea floor round the foot of the kelp the divers discover another problem. Sea urchins. These long-spined creatures are voracious and aggressive grazers on kelp, feeding relentlessly until the plants are wiped out. Normally sea urchins inhabit the warmer waters further north and don't thrive in Tasmania's cold temperatures, but as the waters here warm up, the urchins are invading. It's a double whammy. Now nearly half

OPPOSITE *None of the dive team had ever seen a weedy sea dragon. But they struck lucky at the very end of the dive. Philippe Cousteau and Tooni Mahto make the most of the extraordinary sight of this rare and elusive creature.*

the total kelp here has disappeared, and in some areas over 95 per cent has vanished. It's daunting to think that a warming of just 1.5°C has led to this devastation.

And recently overfishing has made the situation even worse. Rock lobsters are the only natural predators of the urchins, and many of these have been removed by intensive fishing. As a result, the number of sea urchins has exploded. With no predators, the urchins rampage unchecked, stripping vast areas of kelp. Along the coast, especially the northern areas, sea urchins have removed all the kelp – leading to vast areas of 'urchin barrens'. Already some species of fish that depend on the kelp are vanishing, among them the red handfish – a curious fish that 'walks' on its fins – and the magpie perch.

As the divers retreat to the surface they are dismayed by the wholesale destruction of this unique habitat, and the threat it brings to the many creatures that depend on it for their own survival.

DRAGONS DEN

The weedy sea dragon is an almost mythical creature, related to the sea horse, which is found only in the kelp forests of the Southern Ocean. It is rare and elusive, its bizarre frond-like projections making it perfectly adapted to the seaweed in which it hides. And despite several dives into the kelp the divers had failed to get even a single glimpse of these quaint creatures. None of them had ever seen a sea dragon, and, given the state of the kelp, this could be the last chance ever to find one. It was nearly dusk, but time for just one last dive.

The weedy sea dragon is a very slow-moving animal, so it depends for its survival on camouflage. With its straggly shape and long frond-like appendages it is identical to the kelp. It hovers, perfectly still, deep inside the fronds of the kelp, virtually invisible. For a moment finding one seems an almost laughable quest: like searching for a four-leafed clover in a vast meadow. But then a tiny movement, just the merest flicker of an eye, and there it is – a weedy sea dragon. It is an incredible sight: gloriously, riotously coloured, red and yellow with hints of blue along its ribbed back. It drifts effortlessly through the water, the tiny movement of its fin barely perceptible.

Each sea dragon has a unique face with its own distinctive pattern of spots.

Each sea dragon has a unique face with its own distinctive pattern of spots. Sea dragons are related to the sea horse but, unlike them, they do not have a pouch for rearing their young. Instead, the males carry the eggs fixed to the underside of their tails until they hatch. They feed on tiny crustaceans and other zooplankton which they suck into the end of their long tube-like snouts. Watching the sea dragon is magical, and the divers stay until it finally drifts off into the seaweed.

The weedy sea dragon is just one of the many species that depend on the kelp ecosystem to survive. It's a curious irony that, while most of us are aware of the threat of losing the rainforests on land, across the world few people care, or even know, of the destruction of this vital ecosystem in our seas.

PLANE TRUTH

There's a mystery to be solved here. Why are parts of this ocean warming up faster than the other oceans of the world? Estimates suggest that globally sea temperatures have risen by an average of 0.6°C. Here the rise is 1.5°C. The expedition is teaming up with scientists Dr Ken Ridgway, Simon Allen and Lindsay MacDonald from CSIRO Marine and Atmospheric Research to help with an experiment.

They've brought a glider. But this glider is designed for the sea, not the air. It's an underwater remote temperature sensor, fitted with GPS, a motor and wings. It is capable of adjusting its buoyancy to sink to depths of 200 metres before gliding back along pre-programmed trajectories collecting data as it goes and relaying it back to the research team by satellite. The team's task is to set it off on its first 'test flight'. As recently as 1998, scientists identified a powerful warm water current, the Eastern Australia current. As its name suggests, this current flows around eastern Australia and the northern reaches of Tasmania, but there are now indications that it's on the move. The aim of the glider research is to track this movement.

Previous research, measuring the current at different points suggests that the warm waters are being driven further south – a warm 'tongue' reaching right into the Southern Ocean along the coast of Tasmania. It's this change of the current's direction that is causing the waters here to heat so quickly. The shift of the current seems to be the result of stronger South Pacific winds that are driving it further south. At first sight, therefore, the warming appears to have little to do with climate change. But some scientists suggest that ocean winds may have become stronger as a result of both higher concentrations of greenhouse gases in the atmosphere and long-term ozone depletion in the stratosphere. The warming waters here are the result of a complex chain of events that starts with human activity releasing greenhouse gases, which leads to increased winds, to the shift of a critical current, to the decimation of a habitat and, eventually to the potential loss of the fascinating weedy sea dragon and many other species.

> The warming waters here are the result of … human activity releasing greenhouse gases …

RECOVERING SEAL POPULATION

Faced with the bleak outlook for the kelp and its linked ecosystems, it is hard to feel optimistic. However, there are signs of a brighter future, at least for some creatures. As the *Odalisque* makes for our next destination, ploughing through the seas, the team is surprised by a huge colony of Australian fur seals. The first encounter is aural – the sound of their coarse and deafening barking. But as the boat rounds the cove, there they are – a vast throng of noisy, busy, energetic seals, clambering all over the rocks, and diving and splashing in the sea. The Australian fur seal is the fourth rarest seal in the world. It was hunted to the brink of extinction in the last century, and the recovery of the population has been slow. So it is an exceptional delight to see such a thriving large colony.

OPPOSITE *Hunted to the brink of extinction in the last century, the population of Australian fur seals in the Southern Ocean is recovering.*

BIRTH OF AN OCEAN

Having seen a glimpse of the future of this ocean, the expedition's next objective is to travel into its past. The *Odalisque* sets sail along the Tasman Peninsula. The team is planning to investigate the birth of the Southern Ocean itself. Part of this extraordinary story lies deep inside sea caves that drill into the foot of massive rocky cliffs. As the boat passes by, these cliffs and rock-stacks along the shoreline tower 300 metres above it with unusual rock formations. Huge hexagonal columns of basalt rock jut out from the water – very similar in structure to the Giant's Causeway off the coast of Ireland. The huge columns are actually giant magma crystals known as dolerite. Tasmania has the largest and most extensive dolerite formations anywhere in the world.

Waterfall Bay is a relatively small bay about 2½ miles south of Eaglehawk Neck. Below sea level this coast is marked by a series of submarine caves. And in these lies evidence of how the Southern Ocean was formed. About 300

million years ago, tectonic activity lifted up the eastern side of the peninsula. As it did so, it trapped sea creatures, which were then fossilized in the rocks. Now those fossils are deep under the sea, in the labyrinth of sea caves under the cliffs.

The fossils here are a diverse range of ancient sea creatures including brachiopods, bryozoans (coral-like colonies), bivalves like molluscs, and gastropods. The ones the *Oceans* team is interested in are the brachiopods, small two-shelled marine creatures that resemble modern-day clams though they are not closely related. These brachiopods are a time capsule. They date from around 300 million years ago during the Devonian period and survived right up to the beginning of the Jurassic period around 160 million years ago. Throughout this time they went through distinct and rapid evolution creating a series of specific forms of brachiopod, which can be precisely dated. This makes them an ideal index fossil for dating specific geological formations.

When one of the fossil rocks that the divers brought up from a sea cave was broken open, something rather remarkable emerged: a brachiopod fossil, very specifically linked to one point in geological time and, surprisingly, exactly the same as brachiopods found in the Antarctic – over 1,860 miles away. It's crucial evidence that at one time Tasmania and the Antarctic were linked together as one land mass and that the Southern Ocean had yet to exist at all. This fossil is a moment from ancient history, when one vast continent, Gondwana, dominated the southern hemisphere. This huge piece of land, which included the land masses that would become Africa, Antarctica, India and South America, was gradually broken apart by massive geological forces. The land masses went their separate ways, with New Zealand breaking away 80 million years ago and Australia splitting from Antarctica about 45 million years ago. Tasmania was the last land mass to separate from Antarctica, and the Southern Ocean was formed.

As Tasmania drifted away, it left one single, uninterrupted sea circling the entire globe. The Antarctic circumpolar current evolved, and the Southern Ocean became the only place in the world with a fully circular current. This vast current deflected warm waters away from Antarctica, which gradually became iced over forming the southern polar ice cap.

And in our hands, on the grubby dive deck of the *Odalisque*, we are holding tiny fossils that tell that epic story.

> This fossil is a moment from ancient history, when one vast continent, Gondwana, dominated the southern hemisphere.

Diving into History

It seemed incredible that I could get close to the Antarctic and begin to truly understand the birth of the Southern Ocean and the emergence of all its marine life by diving sea caves under the Tasman Peninsula. But our research notes showed us that the key was to find some particular rocks on a cave floor. Easy, until you think about how these sea caves evolved. The rock is dolerite, formed by molten magma being squeezed to the surface between continental plates and then cooling rapidly. It's amazingly hard stuff and at the top of Friedrich Moh's rock strength table. The Egyptians used balls of it to cut granite to build the pyramids.

For millions of years the sea has been pounding these cliffs with seemingly little effect. But in a few rare spots it has found a weakness, maybe a tiny fissure where the molten rock formed around a small imperfection. The relentless sea exploited this weakness, first pounding it into a small crack and then into larger holes, until eventually a great, complex cave system was developed. It makes sense but it's still very difficult to believe when you see it.

On the floor of one of these caves were our elusive rocks. The trouble was that the powerful waves and surges that created the caves long ago still exist and make diving dangerous. Local knowledge says you can only dive in these caves when the surge is less than half a metre. There have been spectacular accidents, with experienced divers getting tangled in their safety lines, the surges wrapping them up in a rope cocoon, disorienting them in the foam at the top of the caves and spitting them out dead weeks later.

We had a surge of about 2 metres and had anchored our dive boat about 10 metres from the cliff wall. We rode the swells more or less comfortably, but the waves reflecting back from the cliffs seemed to induce seasickness in almost everyone. An occasional bigger surge seemed to come from nowhere, so I agreed to do a reconnaissance dive to check out the conditions.

It was fine away from the cliffs, but as soon as I got near the sea wall I knew this would not work. I had no control whatsoever. As the current shot me past the entrance it felt as if I was going to be sucked in. And once inside I would have little chance of escape. It was clear we had to wait for the surges to die down. I did not want to move the boat, as our position was perfect. So we hung on. We had a huge stroke of luck after about two hours when the surges began to lose their power and we were able to make a second attempt. Tooni and I descended into the wonderful world of the swaying kelp forests and it was immediately obvious that this time the conditions were workable.

> … the waves reflecting back from the cliffs seemed to induce seasickness in almost everyone.

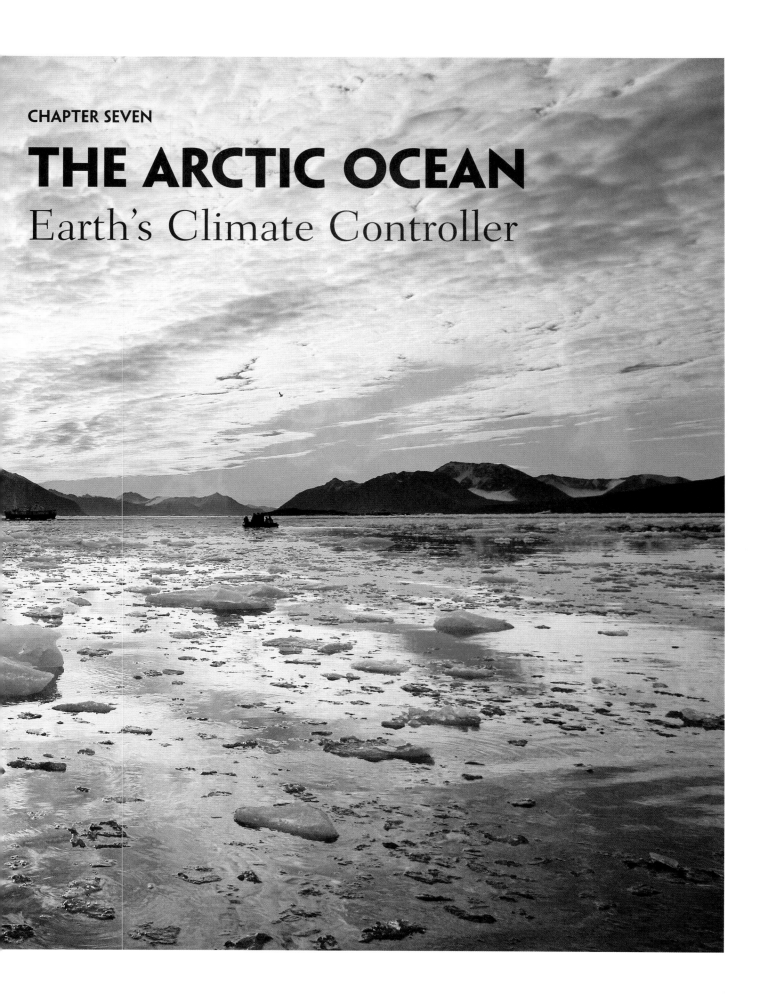

CHAPTER SEVEN

THE ARCTIC OCEAN
Earth's Climate Controller

ABOVE *This satellite image shows the maximum extent of the ice on the Arctic Ocean in 2006. Ice cover has reduced further since then, at an alarming 37,300 square miles a year.*

OPPOSITE *Polar bear tracks on the ice near the* Lance's *mooring. The tracks reinforced the team's need for armed guards when members were working out on the ice.*

PREVIOUS PAGE *Icy wastes at Svalbard in the Arctic Ocean, once one of the world's major whaling grounds.*

THE SOUL-SPLITTING GRAUNCH that rings out as thick ice splinters makes it feel as if the earth itself is ripping asunder. There's the residue of an uncomfortable echo over chilly polar seas while the boat's sharp prow continues to scythe through pack ice. The *Oceans* expedition team has gathered on the deck of the ice-breaker *Lance* at 2 a.m., unable to sleep in the round-the-clock daylight of the Arctic midsummer. All around there bear tracks are imprinted on the surface of the ice heading off towards the horizon, the sole sign of life in this white wilderness.

Suddenly the maker of the tracks appears, the largest land carnivore on the planet and among the few species known to attack humans. This polar bear stands tall and shaggy, and is less than 10 metres from the ship. Silhouetted against the night sunlight, the undisputed master of this blank, white environment looms large and menacing. The team had arrived in the Arctic and was face to face with its most iconic inhabitant. Indeed, the Arctic, derived from the ancient Greek word *arktikos*, means land of the great bear. Weighing in at about 1760 pounds, he cuts an impressive figure.

PREVIOUS PAGES *Top of the food chain: polar bears are perfectly adapted to life in the frozen wastes of the Arctic – the 'land of the great bear'.*

RIGHT *Polar bear fur is, in fact, devoid of colour, they appear white because of the way it reflects light.*

BELOW *The* Lance *at anchor some 500 miles from the North Pole. The team came this far north so that they could investigate the state of older and, so far, permanent multi-year ice.*

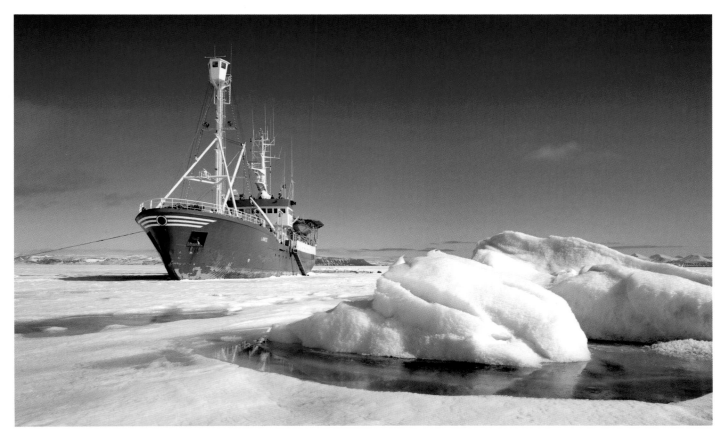

Most ice-thickness measurements come from remote satellite mapping, so data collected directly from the pack ice is very valuable in monitoring the rate at which the ice caps are melting. Ice forms over several years. Multi-year ice is thicker and more stable than first-year ice, which can melt swiftly.

Under water there are signs of melting. In places the ice cover has thinned drastically, forming blue melt ponds where the light cascades down through sea 'skylights'. Scalloped formations are visible at the edges of ridges, a result of fluid flow and heat transfer just adjacent to the ice. There are several signs that this is young ice. Overall, it is flatter than older ice, there are fewer large keels and deep ridges, and those are more jagged and sharper as they haven't been weathered by the action of waves. The thinner ice is less blue than the thicker ice because it contains more salt. Over time the salt in the ice drains out, leaving fresh water. Some old ice was fresh enough for polar explorers to have used it as drinking water. Frozen fresh water scatters light differently and appears blue, as do freshwater glaciers.

On the surface of the ice, members of the team are taking direct measurements of its thickness by boring holes through it. They will take several core samples over a wide area, but first comes the all-important 'taste test'. Ice from the cores can be melted and tasted like a fine wine. The more salty it is, the younger the ice. The water here is certainly salty and a more thorough salinity test confirms that the ice is likely to be young. For the direct measurements, four separate holes are drilled across the ice floe and a line is dropped down to the bottom of the ice. Anything more than 2–3 metres would indicate multi-year ice that's been laid down over several seasons and is less likely to melt. But the readings are all much less – 1.76 metres, 1.60, 1.56, 1.65. The floe comprises thin, first-year ice and is unlikely to be around for long. This confirms the satellite surveys. In 2008 the majority of the ice cover of the Arctic was thin ice, which is likely to melt with even a fractional temperature increase. It's more evidence of the erosion of the permanent ice cap, a recent and disturbing trend. Scientists once estimated that by 2030 the cap would have completely disappeared for parts of the year. But the ice is thinning so rapidly that a recent study by American scientists suggests this could be as soon as 2013.

The loss of ice cover in the Arctic has many profound consequences. As well as speeding up global warming as more heat is absorbed by the oceans and land, it also has a dramatic impact on the ocean circulation across the planet. All our oceans are linked into one vast ocean system. Heat and nutrients are transported around the world on powerful ocean currents that act like conveyors, and the Arctic is one of the major engines of this ocean circulation. When sea ice forms, salt is released

OPPOSITE, TOP The world's oceans are linked into one vast system. Water is driven around the planet by temperature and water density – this is called the thermohaline circulation system. The Arctic acts as one of this system's major engines, cooling water that flows north from the Atlantic and pushing it southwards towards the tropics.

OPPOSITE, BOTTOM When two pack ice floes meet the ice is forced up into mounds of 'boulders'; this is similar to when tectonic plates press together to form hills or mountains on land.

It's more evidence of the erosion of the permanent ice cap, a recent and disturbing trend.

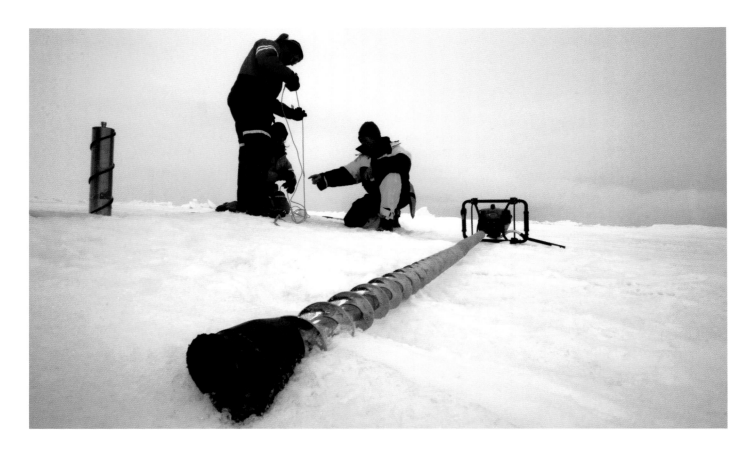

ABOVE *The team bored holes into the ice to test its thickness and to take core samples. The ice was thin, first-year ice, which is more prone to melting.*

into the ocean water making it more dense. This cold, dense polar water sinks and moves along the ocean bottom towards the Atlantic and on to the tropics where it drives heat from the warm tropical waters around the world's oceans. The entire system is called the thermohaline circulation and is vital for the distribution of heat around the planet. This helps to control the climate and weather of the world, which in turn directly affects the lives and livelihoods of every one of us. A reduction in the amount of sea ice combined with the resulting influx of fresh water from the melt could reduce the amount of Arctic water that sinks, slowing down the thermohaline circulation.

On the evening of the dive the team gathered on the boat in the glare of the 24-hour daylight and it seemed the empty, white wilderness couldn't be more remote from the rest of the planet. And yet, as we were learning, we were in the heart of its weather engine. So much of the world's welfare and our way of life is intimately connected with this unknown, isolated outpost.

SPRING BLOOM

The divers were back under the ice the next day and this time they were looking for life. The Arctic is one of the most hostile habitats in the world and yet, surprisingly, the ice itself is teeming with small to minuscule forms of life, all perfectly adapted to these extreme conditions.

The physical and biological properties of this ocean are unique, with extreme ranges of light and year-round ice cover. So life forms in the ice have made some remarkable adaptations. Since the organisms are the same temperature as the ice, their survival depends on preventing ice crystals forming in their bodies during the cold winter months. Many organisms have special proteins in their blood that act as a kind of anti-freeze, and accumulate large deposits of fats or fatty material to stop themselves freezing. Food is scarce here so some are sufficiently evolved to survive up to ten months of starvation.

Food is scarce here so some are sufficiently evolved to survive up to ten months of starvation.

There is one short annual pulse of prolific life, known as the spring bloom. The ice cover is reduced, the sun is out and nature makes the most of it. The nutrient-rich waters are exposed to high light levels, creating a bloom of phytoplankton that trails the edges of the ice and can stretch for more than 30 miles.

Microscopic algae grow in high concentrations on the underside of the ice, attached to ice crystals and pockets of salt water in the ice. Ice algae have a higher concentration of fats than phytoplankton, so are a rich food source. Inside the microscopic algae are even smaller diatoms. These have photosynthetic pigments that use the light to generate energy. Diatoms are considered the most important primary producers of energy within the ice, with more than 200 species occurring in the Arctic.

The Arctic spring bloom is short and the further north you go, the shorter and later the season. So energy is available in huge quantities but only for a limited time. The Arctic calanoid copepod has adapted specially to this. The tiny invertebrate eats the food available during the bloom and stores the energy in the form of energy-rich lipids. It then lives off these fat stores for the rest of the year, while providing year-round food for the rest of the food chain.

THE HUMBLE AMPHIPOD

The creatures the expedition is interested in are slightly further up the food chain – the Arctic amphipods. Like the rest of life here, these tiny crustaceans are specially adapted to live in the unstable and extreme conditions of the pack ice. They have a ponderously slow metabolic rate, due to limited food availability and the low temperatures, and to secure reproduction in this harsh environment they live longer than other organisms, with some amphipods reaching the ripe old age of five years. And to further maximize the chances of successful reproduction, males and females spend most of their life swimming close together. Amphipods will eat anything – algae, detritus in the water, and even, perhaps, each other. It's thought that junior amphipods of one species colonize new ice in order to avoid being eaten by adults.

Amphipods are hugely important because they are the main link to the major animals of the Arctic. They provide food for fish like the polar cod. These are then eaten by larger marine creatures, like seals and whales, who themselves are the food of the apex predators such as orca whales and polar bears. It's a complex food web, and it all starts in a very small way with the tiny life forms in the sea ice.

> Like canaries in a gold mine, these vital creatures will be the first to die.

If current climate change predictions are correct, the reduced sea-ice cover will be a major problem for the amphipods that inhabit it. Like canaries in a gold mine, these vital creatures will be the first to die, signalling the hazards ahead. And, as they are a primary link in the food chain, their extinction will have a fundamental knock-on effect on all life in the Arctic, from fish to polar bears.

The divers' task was to collect specimens of the amphipod populations and other ice creatures, for the Arctic Ocean Biodiversity Project. Current knowledge of Arctic biodiversity is limited and has significant gaps. But now, with the tremendous ongoing changes to the Arctic Ocean, the

RIGHT *The old whaling ground at Svalbard is littered with the relics of a trade that was at its height in the seventeenth century. Once the water here was teeming with whales.*

The amphipod is a vital link in the food chain that keeps all creatures of the Arctic alive. Amphipods are specially adapted to life in the pack ice and their survival depends on it. Current reductions in the ice cover here puts them seriously at risk.

effort to identify the diversity of life there has become an urgent issue. Collecting samples of the vibrant life living in and around the ice itself was no easy task. Most of it is tiny to the point of being invisible to the naked eye. But eventually a significant number of voucher specimens had been collected, all of which will be recorded and act as baseline data to monitor changes in biodiversity.

The tiny amphipod, curled over like a prawn, is a crucial part of life in the Arctic. As the ice retreats many of us think only of the polar bear. Perhaps we should be more worried about the humble amphipod.

Diving at minus 1.8°C

I woke with a start when I felt the ship move. Knowing the vessel was firmly anchored when I went to sleep, I threw on some kit and ran on to the deck into the blinding daylight of four o'clock in the morning to investigate. At first glance everything seemed normal. We were surrounded by polar pack ice, there was no wind and I could hear the ice grinding in the background as it always does. But we were slowly rotating around the huge ice floe when we should have been immobile.

Looking over the port side I could see that our forward line was loose and the wooden holding pole I had drilled 2 metres into the ice was lying flat on the surface of the floe. I leant further over the rail to see a polar bear grunting as he finished pulling out the midships anchor. Then he lumbered away to the stern anchor to complete the job of casting us loose. It took me a few moments to take this in, so by the time I had raised the alarm the bear was sauntering off into the distance.

I cast a wary eye along the horizon, looking for more bears.

As we reset the anchors I cast a wary eye along the horizon, looking for more bears. But it's almost impossible to see them out on the ice, as they blend so well with the pressure ridges and windblown features of the polar landscape. It certainly reinforced the need for our armed polar bear guards to be on duty at all times when we were out on the ice.

We had spent days breaking a route north in the dense ice pack and we were now at 81°N, 540 miles from the North Pole. Coming this far north was important as we needed to dive under multi-year ice so that we could study its formation, collect some of the life living underneath it, and take core samples from the surface to play our part in a NASA remote-sensing experiment. It also meant that we would be diving in water that was minus 1.8°C, the freezing point of sea water.

… the preparation … creates a sense of focus that gives me a huge amount of energy.

I love the preparation that takes place before a challenging dive as it clears my mind completely. It creates a sense of focus that gives me a huge amount of energy, which I know is what keeps me alive. Diving under ice requires more planning and organization than open water diving as the equipment, diving techniques and safety procedures have to be spot on.

With solid ice all the way to the North Pole and for 60 miles heading south, we had found a small pool of open water, about 7 metres by 2 metres. This was perfect for our diving as it would save hours of cutting through the 2 metre-thick ice. I jumped in and was immediately struck by the lack of visibility. I had hoped for fabulous clarity but I could only see a few metres ahead because of the profusion of algae that added a greenish tinge to the water.

Once I was a good distance under the ice I held my breath a few times to see if I could hear whale song. I had heard this many times diving under Antarctic ice and was keen to enjoy it in the north. But all I heard was the grinding of the polar pack as billions of tonnes of ice moved with ominous force. The movement is generated by the Beaufort gyre, the

OPPOSITE *Paul Rose swims through the icy Arctic water. He was surprised at the lack of under sea visibility caused by the profusion of algae that lives in the water and that gives the sea here its green tinge.*

great clockwise current that circles the entire Arctic Ocean. Along with the Arctic weather systems, polar-pack movement caused by the Beaufort gyre pushes the pack ice together and makes great ridges on its surface and on its bottom. I was now swimming past these under-ice ridges, which act like keels to the floes.

By following the ice keels I found areas where huge floes had overlapped each other and made caves and tunnels. Squeezing through to explore these caves in the ice just added to the fabulous sense of putting the Arctic Ocean into a personal perspective.

As I emerged from the pool I could see that the surface team had been far more uncomfortable than me, as there was a wind and the air was full of blowing snow. We warmed up before we began a series of dives to take measurements and collect samples of marine life.

Aside from the algae, I hadn't been able to see any life on the first dive. Then Jorgen, our science adviser from the Norwegian Polar Institute, told me that the amphipods we were hoping to find were white. So, of course, they were almost impossible to see. On the next dive, I changed my collection technique and kept the net open all the time, waving it around under the ice and hoping I was getting something.

When it comes to the Arctic Ocean we are in a race against time. The ice is disappearing fast. Within our lifetimes the region will become unrecognizable. Trans-Arctic will be the normal route for shipping and the loss of the ice will be a massive driver in changing the rest of the earth's climate. So it is essential that we learn and understand as much as possible about the Arctic Ocean ecosystem while we can. It felt good to know that even randomly waving a big net was helping this research.

I handed the net over to Jorgen, hoping there was something useful in it, and got busy working on my dive gear, packing the surface support unit and thinking about clearing the team off the ice and moving the ship south. Once aboard there was a huge amount to do — but I couldn't resist the temptation to check in with Jorgen. 'Anything useful in the samples?' I asked, casually. Pointing to the collection jar he said, 'A ja! Dette er en ny art!' (Oh yes! This one is a new species!).

MOBILE MENACE

There's another, more insidious threat to Arctic life and it's one that's only recently been identified. Industrial pollutants, including cadmium, mercury, lead, caesium, uranium, organophosphates and coolants, properly called polychlorinated biphenyls or PCBs, are turning up in the body tissues of creatures throughout the food chain.

Although it is generally a pristine environment, pollutants are blown to the Arctic or brought by the ocean currents from industrialized nations further south. Cold temperatures mean that contaminants are slow to break down and the lack of sunlight further lengthens the degradation process. Both factors increase the likelihood that toxic chemicals will find their way into the food chain.

More problematic still is the fact that these poisons are largely fat-soluble and all Arctic animals have plenty of fat. Everything from amphipods to the polar bear is relatively long-lived, so toxins build up to dangerous levels and are concentrated as they travel up through the food web. Compared to land-based ecosystems, the food chain in the Arctic is complex with many layers, so animals at the top of the food web eat all the chemicals consumed by their prey, and their prey's prey, building up high concentrations of poisons.

While the levels of toxic compounds are still fairly minimal among lower orders – less than those found in other oceans of the world – they are significant in seals and are troublingly high in predators like killer whales and polar bears. No one knows what impact this is having on the health of animals in the Arctic, but studies of humans and animals under laboratory conditions have shown the disturbing effects of these pollutants. For a start, they appear to interfere with the production of sex hormones, affecting reproduction rates and the health of the young. They can inhibit the workings of the immune system, reducing the ability to fight disease, and can lead to skin damage, impairment of the nervous system and increased tumour rates. While it's difficult to assess the impact of toxic compounds on the wildlife here directly, the laboratory evidence provides a stark warning sign. When it comes to pollution, this remote wilderness, it seems, is not nearly remote enough.

The *Lance* is moving south now, away from the pack ice to the fjords of Svalbard in search of one of the Arctic's most engaging marine animals: the beluga whale. The name derives from the Russian word *belukha*, which means white, reflecting the animal's ghostly hue after a summer moult. Sometimes belugas are known as white whales.

toxic compounds …
are troublingly high
in predators like
killer whales and
polar bears.

OPPOSITE *Following the ice keels allowed Paul Rose to access the caves and tunnels formed underneath the ice when huge floes overlap.*

WHALE WATCH

Like most creatures of the Arctic beluga whales depend on ice, feeding around the edges of glaciers and the fast ice connected to shorelines. They also depend on tiny amphipods, existing at the rear end of the food chain. The amphipods feed the polar cod and polar cod is one of the main sources of food for belugas.

The population of belugas in Svalbard is notoriously shy, being unused to human contact. Belugas are even thought to actively avoid boats, so although they are easily distinguishable by colour spotting any will be a challenge. Two boats are sent out to scour the likely feeding grounds but, after watching and waiting for hours in the bitter cold and biting wind, there is no sign of the whales. Instead, a bearded seal is spotted, resting on an ice floe, his face ruddy from snuffling about on the sea floor where iron deposits have collected in the sediment. These stick to the seal's whiskers and oxidize to rust in the air, turning these sober-faced creatures gingery red. Bearded seals are common in the Arctic, and are the largest of all the seal species found here, with an average weight of around 440 pounds.

> The population of belugas in Svalbard is notoriously shy, being unused to human contact.

But it's not seals the team are trying to find and there's a sense of frustration that they haven't seen any beluga. They are almost ready to abandon all hope when someone catches a glimpse of something white breaching the surface of the water a short distance away. At last, a beluga whale breaks cover. And not just one as, typically, belugas are social creatures who travel in an average pod size of ten. More and more appear until the team are surrounded by about 30 whales glistening white and arcing in the waters of the bay.

Belugas may not be the largest of whales but a group of them still cuts an impressive spectacle. Males can reach about 4.5 metres in length and weigh around 3300 pounds. They have several talents, including being able to swim forwards and backwards, and the ability to survive in shallow water. But perhaps their most charming characteristic is the high-pitched clicks, whistles, twitters and clangs with which they communicate.

> Belugas resemble dolphins and, like them, appear friendly with a gentle 'smile'.

Belugas resemble dolphins and, like them, appear friendly with a gentle 'smile'. They have square, blunt heads and a prominent, oil-filled 'melon' that they use for echolocation. They are able to change the shape of the melon by blowing air around their sinuses and this, rather oddly, allows them to change their facial expression. It's thought that belugas do this, just as we do, to display different moods like aggression or appeasement.

As the team watched the belugas they could see how perfectly they are designed for the hostile, harsh Arctic. These whales have a huge layer of blubber that insulates them against freezing water temperatures. Up to 40 per cent of body weight is blubber and it forms a layer up to 15 centimetres thick under their skins. The skin itself is remarkable, being ten times thicker than that of any other marine mammal and 100 times thicker than that of terrestrial mammals. It is an active, cork-like organ used for insulation, storage of high quantities of vitamin C, and possibly as protection against abrasion caused by the ice. Like other Arctic whales (bowhead whales and narwhals) the beluga has no visible dorsal fin. This might be to reduce the surface area over which heat could be lost, or simply to make swimming through the ice-covered water easier.

ABOVE *A pod of beluga whales. These social animals, at home in the cold waters of the Arctic, depend on ice, feeding in the waters on the edges of glaciers and the fast ice connected to the shoreline.*

Recently it was thought that belugas restricted themselves to open sea or areas of loosely packed ice, but satellite tracking has revealed that they can move relatively rapidly in heavy pack ice, looking for thin slivers of open water where they can feed. They are remarkably efficient at finding these tiny openings, but how they do it is still a mystery. We can only presume that echolocation is the key.

Cold and discomfort are completely forgotten as the team watches these gracious beasts, elegantly and effortlessly cutting through this harsh ocean. Currently the population in Svalbard is thriving as belugas are a protected species here. But across many areas of the Arctic commercial hunting of belugas continues and as a result their numbers are declining.

Over the years, whaling has caused the destruction of whale populations and some have never recovered. The *Lance* has arrived at a blowy, snowy outpost along the shores of the Svalbard, which was once the heart of the first intensive whaling operation in the Arctic. Smeerenburg, meaning Blubber Town, is now an empty, desolate stretch of shore but in the seventeenth century it was a thriving settlement. Its wealth was built on one thing: the capture, killing and processing of whales.

… commercial hunting of belugas continues and as a result their numbers are declining.

WHALING NATIONS

Standing on the beach and looking out to sea, it's hard to imagine that these waters were once heaving with whales. But early in the seventeenth century that's what drew Dutch and English whalers to this part of the Arctic. Smeerenburg was a Dutch outpost servicing up to 250 whaling ships. When whaling there was at its height (up to about the mid-seventeenth century) 200 people lived in the town and there are still the remains of huge furnaces that were used to melt the whale blubber into commercially valuable whale oil. The oil was used for light, heat, soap, cosmetics and industrial lubricants. Further, it featured in the preparation of rope, cloth and textiles, and as a mixing agent in pigments and paints. Gradually use was even found for the baleen, the bony plate at the roof of the whale's mouth that filters the zooplankton: it hugged the tiny waists of Victorian women in the form of stays in corsets.

Originally, whales were caught near to shore and processed on land in Smeerenburg and other towns, but as the industry developed in the second half of the century it moved to the open water. Whales were flensed (stripped of blubber) alongside whaling ships and the blubber was frequently boiled on the vessel to make oil.

Fuelled by the high price of the oil, whaling operations were intensive. Over the course of 200 or 300 years 122,000 whales were killed. Soon there were so few whales it became impossible to make a living, and the trade dried up, leaving many species permanently decimated. One species that was

OPPOSITE *The 'smiley' beluga is often thought to resemble a dolphin. But the blunt oil-filled melon at the front of its head houses a sophisticated echolocation system.*

LEFT *This early nineteenth century illustration shows a whale hunt in progress, with a man in the prow of the boat about to throw his harpoon.*

particularly affected got its name from the whaling operations: the Greenland right whale. This vast creature, also known as the bowhead, is between 12 and 18 metres long and weighs between 50 and 100 tonnes. But despite its colossal size it is easy prey. It moves slowly in the water, and when dead it doesn't sink but floats on the surface. And it has a rich, thick layer of blubber. This made it the 'right' whale to hunt, the 'right' whale to kill. Once 46,000 of these lived around the waters of Spitzbergen. But the population was annihilated by the whaling industry. Despite the decline of the whale trade and the moratorium on whaling in the 1960s, the bowhead population has never really recovered. Now, there are fewer than 10,000 whales across the entire Arctic, and virtually none in the waters around Svalbard.

Now, there are fewer than 10,000 whales across the entire Arctic ...

WALRUS WONDERLAND

There's another Arctic creature whose story is much more positive: the vast, ungainly mass of blubber and tusk that is better known as the walrus. Walrus were also hunted intensively for their meat, skin, tusks, fat and bone, and by the middle of the nineteenth century, the population had plunged. By the time hunting stopped in 1952, they were on the point of extinction with only about 100 individuals left in the Arctic. Although numbers are still low, the protected population here is thriving and growing. And as food sources are plentiful they can continue to thrive; in short, there are plenty enough clams for everybody.

Walrus feed in shallow waters and on truffle bivalve molluscs like clams and mussels, which live on the sea bottom. Compared to the barren waste on land, the sea floor of the Arctic Ocean abounds with colourful life, especially in the shallower waters. Coralline algae – filter-feeding invertebrates – anemones and soft corals create a riot of colour. The cold waters are rich in nutrients and here the divers are surrounded by vibrant life. Crabs, sea cucumbers, sea lilies and sponges, as well as the clams and mussels loved by walrus, are abundant. Rich algae like kelp stream in the cold currents and a blaze of sea anemones and corals is breathtaking. Yet again, this extreme, isolated, apparent wilderness has upended any preconceptions.

As the expedition comes to an end and we return to warmer climes, we recognize that this trip has revealed a remarkable ocean, one that seems distant and remote yet is intimately connected to the lives of people all over the globe. An ocean that seems harsh and extreme yet supports a vibrant abundance of life – and one that appears pristine and untouched but is under threat, not from its own pollution but from ours.

OPPOSITE *The walrus is ungainly on land but awe-inspiring under the water. A fully grown male has tusks up to 40 centimetres long which it uses to spar with its rivals when finding a mate.*

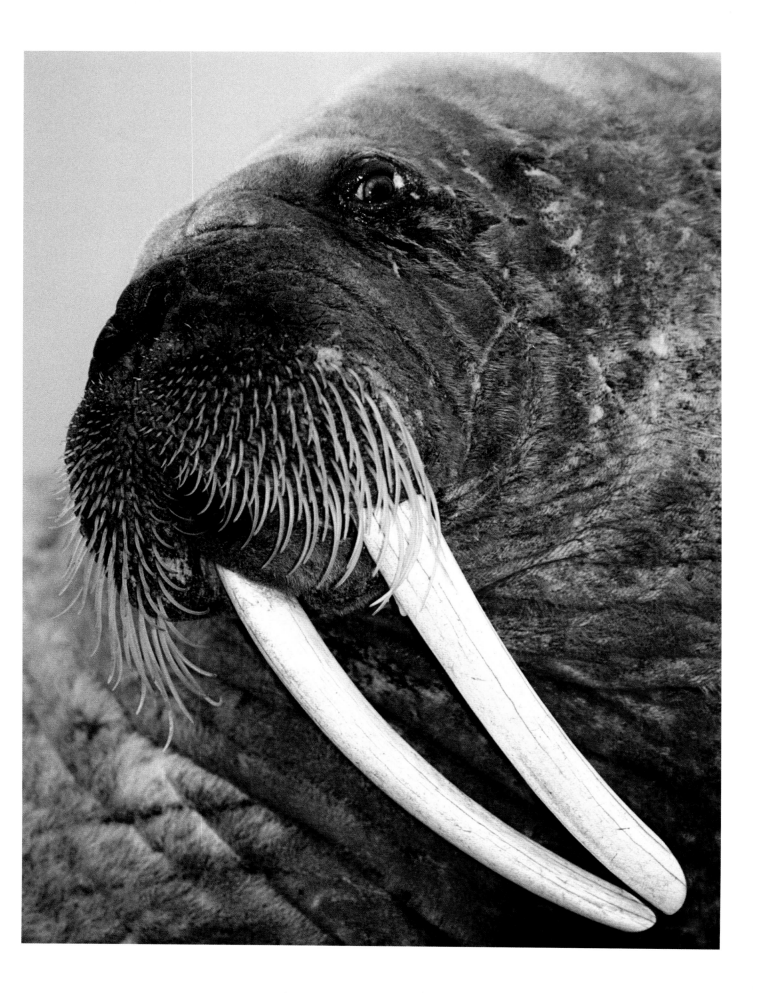

Paul Rose versus the Walrus

Tooni and I had been fortunate to get very close to a group of about 40 walrus on the beach. We had started downwind of the beach so they couldn't smell us, kept ourselves very low so they couldn't see us, and had also been careful not to get between them and the sea as we didn't want to be flattened when they headed for the water.

The group comprised all males, as females and calves stay further north in close contact with the pack ice. This behaviour has evolved as a successful strategy to spread the feeding grounds, therefore increasing the likelihood of the young calves' survival. All the walrus were relaxed and seemed very sociable as they squeezed up next to each other. This close-quarter contact is key to communication between them. But they also communicate verbally, and occasionally they all burst into a great variety of snorting, shuffling, sniffing, coughing, growling, grunting, barking, clicking, rasping and even whistling.

They walrus were pale, which indicated that they had just completed a series of long dives to feed on clams. Walrus gorge themselves in bursts of two to three days and, in that time, make about 400 dives and consume a staggering 20,000 clams. After spending about 20 hours on the beach they will return for another feeding session. So walrus have an enviable lifestyle, spending three-quarters of their time at sea feeding and one-quarter on a beach. Before they head back into the sea they return to their usual brown/pink-tinged colour.

Their activity on land is fascinating, and it didn't matter to us in the slightest that it was a cold day complete with gale-force winds. We were as happy to stay on that beach as were the walrus. But I felt we were really missing out if we didn't study them under water. If they spent the majority of their time in the sea, that's where I wanted to see them.

The gale-force wind had whipped up the sea but I felt there was a chance of getting our walrus cage close to the haul-out beach, where there was a calmer eddy. The water looked murky but I thought it was worth a try. We spent a few hours towing the cage through the big seas and positioning it about 25 metres from the beach.

As I prepared to dive I remember saying to Tooni – a tad self-righteously – that this was the real way to study walrus. It's great to be with them on land but you've just got to get in there with them to really appreciate how they move. As ungainly as they are on land they would be like ballerinas when I saw them from my cage.

Tooni was smart enough to stay on the boat, and was having a superb experience studying the group from the seaward side. The moment I entered the cage I knew this was going to be difficult. Visibility was only about a metre. The walrus were very curious about us and came over in groups of three or four. Some were young, with tusks about 10 centimetres long. And then we would get a visit from a huge full-grown male with tusks at a full-sized 40 centimetres. To see these huge animals coming at you from the water

---

Walrus binge-feeding: the numbers

5–7 minutes a single feeding dive
50 clams per single dive
8–9 clams eaten per minute when diving
1 ¾ pounds clam meat per single dive
110–154 pounds clam meat ingested per day
400 dives per feeding trip
20,000 clams per feeding trip

OPPOSITE *Female walruses and their calves live separately from the males so as to spread their feeding grounds – a policy that has been successful in increasing the survival rates of youngsters.*

OVERLEAF *In the Arctic circle summertime heralds 24-hour daylight – this is the midnight sun.*

is awe-inspiring. They are massive and fast. In fact, they can reach a speed of 22 miles per hour.

When the walrus got close I ducked under the surface to see them – but I just could not see anything. I popped up and they were right there; I went down and saw nothing. I had no idea what they would look like under water but imagined they would appear to be incredibly powerful as they swam along to the feeding grounds at high speeds. I was face to face with any number of walrus on the surface and could see some of their behaviours up close. It was fun to watch how they make their eyeballs bulge in order to get a good all-round view. They came so close that I was worried that one might get a tusk caught over the top of my cage. But in the end I had to leave the walrus to their natural element. I had been at this for over an hour and had seen absolutely nothing.

Not only had they beaten me under water, but the walrus are winning in a much more important way, too; they are triumphing as the earth gets warmer because as the sea ice retreats the clam population will increase dramatically. Plus, walrus will get more access to their feeding grounds and more sites where they can haul themselves out of the sea will become available.

> I popped up and they were right there; I went down and saw nothing.

INDEX

Page numbers in **bold** denote illustrations

ACKNOWLEDGEMENTS

This book, like the series on which it is based, is the result of an enormous team effort and we are hugely indebted to so many people for their support and encouragement.

This project could not have happened without the driving force of our series producer – half woman, half human dynamo – Helen Thomas, to whom we are extremely grateful. Huge thanks are also due for the endless hard work and dedication of Rebecca Lavender, Sophie Chapman and Gemma Thomas.

We'd also like to thank the producers of the *Oceans* series, who not only created the individual television episodes, but also kindly read and checked the chapters in the book: Daniel Barry, Matthew Dyas, Matthew Gyves, Milla Harrison, Hannah Robson and Penny Allen. We are more than grateful to the team who trawled the world to bring us the most fascinating marine science: Ruth Dyson, Helene Ganichaud, Ingrid Kvale, Helen Lambourne and Elizabeth Vancura. Particular thanks are also due to Peter Collins for his meticulous work on the drafts of the Red Sea and Atlantic chapters, and Fiona Marsh.

Thanks are due to the people that made the diving safe and possible: Richard Bull, John Chambers, Pete West, Phil Short, Gavin Newman, Brian Kakuk, Wes Skiles and his great team. And to the fantastic camera and sound crew: Scott Tibbles, Mike Kasic, Simon Reynell, Paul Atkins and Michael Pitts. Ian Kellett and Hugh Miller not only assisted and operated the cameras for the shoots, but also took many of the stunning pictures in the book.

The team travelled as a big group with over two tons of equipment and an almost impossible schedule. Thanks are due to all the team's host-nation colleagues, science collaborators, boat captains and crews, local guides and experts.

And of course, thanks to the rest of the presenting team: Lucy Blue – who also took time to read the chapters and make sure they were archaeologically honest – Philippe Cousteau and Tooni Mahto.

Thanks are due to the people who were instrumental in getting the entire project off the ground: BBC commissioner Emma Swain, who drove the development of the idea through to commission, Roly Keating of BBC2 and Martin Davidson. Thanks also to Alison Gregory, who started the project, and to Martin Redfern, who brought us to BBC Books.

At BBC Books we would especially like to thank Karen Farrington for her patient and good-humoured work turning our fractured prose into smooth sentences, and Julian Flanders – a calming and supportive presence who steered this ship beautifully into port. Thanks to David Cottingham who sourced some breathtaking pictures, to Linda Blakemore for her great work on the design, and to Lorna Russell, Muna Reyal and Christopher Tinker, who were hugely encouraging throughout.

On a personal level, Paul would like to thank Nina Ness for providing limitless support and for the steering of the Gonzo factor, his Mum for sound advice, Scott Rose for looking out for him, Nigel Winser of Earthwatch for being his inspiration, David Williams of Impact International for the massive support and the Royal Geographical Society and Marine Education Trust for their encouragement.

Anne would like to thank her family for their unstinting support and encouragement. Her sister Fran for everything, especially the daily texts, and her children Dan and Sezi, who were endlessly patient with an abstracted mother who spent most of her time sweating over a keyboard.

PICTURE CREDITS

Corbis 8–9, 50, 69, 92 (above), 116, 120, 121, 183, 189, 198, 200 (above); **Geoscience Features** 51; **Getty Images** 33, 34, 45, 67, 155 (below), 157, 176–7, 189, 203, 233; **Image Quest Marine** 52–3, 62 Mark Conlon, 81 Carlos Villoch, 87 Mark Conlon, 91 Masa Ushioda, 96 Jeff Yonover, 127 Roger Steene, 145 Jez Tryner, 162–3, 165 (above) Carlos Villoch, 175 Mark Conlon, 231 Kelvin Aitken; **Mary Evans Picture Library** 229; **Naturepl.com** 46 (below) Doug Perrine, 47 Luis Quinta, 56–7 Doug Perrine, 70–1 Onne Van der Wal/Bluegreen, 108–9 Brandon Cole, 150, 152, 153 Marguerite Smits Van Oyen, 174 (above) Jeff Rotman, 179, 181 (above) Roberto Rinaldi/Bluegreen, 187, 188 Vincent Munier, 195 Roberto Rinaldi /Bluegreen, 200 (below) Jurgen Freund, 212 (above) Eric Baccega, 227, 228 Doc White; **Photolibrary Group** 4–5, 22–3, 29 (above), 29 (below), 31, 35, 48–9, 59, 82–3, 88, 99 (above), 114–15, 122, 135, 136–7, 146–7, 149, 181 (below), 182, 190–1, 197, 204, 206–7, 210–11, 234–5; **Science Photolibrary** 12 NOAA, 24, 41, 54, 63, 65, 72, 84, 85, 86, 98, 99 (below), 117, 124–5, 142, 148, 159, 165 (below), 178, 192, 193, 208, 216; **Seapics.com** 3 Doug Perrine, 90 Bob Cranston, 94–5 James D. Watt, 101 Tim Rock, 102 Bob Cranston, 105 Reinhard Dirscherl, 131, 132 Tim Rock, 174 (below) Doug Perrine.

Ian Kellett (BBC) 6, 7, 10, 13, 15, 17, 20, 37, 38, 42, 43, 46 (top), 58, 76, 93, 103, 106, 111, 112, 118, 129, 139, 141, 152, 155 (top), 167, 168, 170, 171, 172, 185, 194, 201, 212, 215, 216, 218, 222, 224
Hugh Miller (BBC) 56, 60, 75, 79 (both), 160–1, 209, 220.

Published to accompany the BBC television series *Oceans*, first broadcast on BBC2 in 2008.
Presenters: Paul Rose, Philippe Cousteau, Lucy Blue and Tooni Mahto
Executive producer: Anne Laking
Series producer: Helen Thomas

10 9 8 7 6 5 4 3 2 1

First published in 2008 by BBC Books, an imprint of Ebury Publishing. A Random House Group Company.

The Random House Group Limited Reg. No. 954009

Addresses for companies within the Random House Group can be found at www.randomhouse.co.uk. A CIP catalogue record for this book is available from the British Library.

ISBN 978 1 84 607505 6

The Random House Group Limited supports the Forest Stewardship Council (FSC), the leading international forest certification organization. All our titles that are printed on Greenpeace approved FSC certified paper carry the FSC logo. Our paper procurement policy can be found at www.rbooks.co.uk/environment

Commissioning editors:
Martin Redfern, Lorna Russell and Muna Reyal
In-house editor: Christopher Tinker
Project editor: Julian Flanders
Copy-editor: Karen Farrington
Designer: Linda Blakemore
Picture researcher: David Cottingham
Maps: Nick Heal
(Base-mapping courtesy of Tom Patterson)
Production: David Brimble

Printed and bound by Butler, Tanner & Dennis Ltd

Colour origination by AltaImage, London

To buy books from your favourite authors and register for offers, visit www.rbooks.co.uk